✱

BELIEVING AND KNOWING

The Meaning of Truth in Biblical Religion and in Science

Iowa State University Press Award for the most significant new book by an Iowa author

Winner, 1965

Teach me good judgment and knowledge
for I believe in thy commandments.

PSALM 119:66

BELIEVING

*

AND KNOWING

The Meaning of Truth in Biblical Religion and in Science

EMERSON W. SHIDELER

The Iowa State University Press/Press Building, Ames, Iowa

1966

ABOUT THE AUTHOR

Emerson W. Shideler is Professor of Philosophy, Iowa State University, where he has taught courses in religion and philosophy since 1950. Besides this book, his writings include articles and critical reviews in *The Christian Century, Journal of Religion, Dialog, Theology Today, Journal of Bible and Religion,* and *Journal of Medical Education.* He is past President of the American Theological Society (Midwest Division). Dr. Shideler is an ordained clergyman in the United Church of Christ (Congregational); he holds the AB degree from the University of Pittsburgh, the BD degree from Chicago Theological Seminary, and the PhD degree from the University of Chicago. Post-doctoral study was at the University of Manchester, England. He was a participant in 1964 at the Institute in Chinese Civilization, Taiwan.

First edition, 1966

Library of Congress Catalog Card Number: 66–14588

FOR MARY

Who gave the resistance of love

✸

TABLE OF CONTENTS

*

INTRODUCTION

THIS BOOK has grown out of my experience as a biblically oriented philosophical theologian trying to talk to the scientists among whom I live and work—and whose students I teach. During these fifteen years, I have become intensely aware that the taproot of the communication problem between scientists and theologians reaches far deeper than surface ignorance of each other's work, pervasive as this may be, and far deeper than questions of church affiliation or views about theism and atheism. Communication and sympathetic understanding between workers in the two fields will not be established by greater diffusion of information about recent scientific findings or the newest theological views. Such informational cures merely sprinkle the surface. They fail to nourish the feeder roots of interrelation between the two fields or their practitioners, because each group thinks in different ways. What is required is to explore the characteristic ways of thought that differentiate each realm of inquiry, because only when one knows *how* the other thinks can he meaningfully relate the findings of the other field to his own work. This book is an essay in this kind of interpretation, beginning from the premise that science and biblical religion are different but related activities, and that no adequate understanding of human existence is possible without the rigorous pursuit of both activities.

My thesis is that the clue to the distinctive character of each discipline lies in the question from which it starts, rather than in a special subject matter that is appropriate to one but not to the other. Science begins with the question of "What is this?" "What kind of thing do we confront?" "What is going on here?" In broad but loose terms, science is descriptive, because the objective of scientific activity is to provide as accurate an account as possible of whatever meets us in our experience. We want to know what is happening to us. We want to know what the source of our experience is, what it is that bumps into us, what is likely to happen next, and perhaps what precautionary steps we should take.

Religion, in the most general sense, begins with a different question: "Who are we?" "How are we to relate ourselves to whatever confronts us?" "How shall we respond in this situation?" This is the question of personal existence whose answer determines our being, and the way we answer it establishes our existence, whether as persons or as something else or as something less.

Biblical religion makes the general religious question specific by asking "How do we respond to the God who is the Lord of human history, who specifically reveals himself in the life, death, and resurrection of Jesus Christ, and who offers man a covenant which threads our history from Sinai to the churches of today?" Biblical religion, as the living participation of a people in this covenant, is not, therefore, primarily a demonstration of God's reality, or a collection of propositions about God and Christ, and it constitutes no completed edifice of truth to be admired and affirmed.

Thus the scientific and religious questions are radically different in kind. In one, man addresses his world of experience; in the other, he himself is addressed. Therefore the answer to one question does not answer the other, and this fact, if taken by itself, would separate science from biblical religion so that they would neither clash nor communicate because they would not meet.

Yet these questions cannot be isolated from each other, because persons act and respond in relationship to something, and it is always legitimate to investigate what that something is. When, as in biblical religion, that something is declared to be the God of concrete human history, both questions cast anchor in the same roadstead of experience.

Some of our difficulties in relating these areas have arisen because we have not seen the fundamental questions; more difficulties have come because we have confused the priority of the questions. Our scientific-minded culture takes it for granted that before one can respond, he must know what he confronts, and on this basis we have first asked whether some scientific demonstration of religion's claims can be accomplished, thereby explicitly forcing religion into a scientific model.

But the scientific question is neither logically nor experientially the first. It seems so because we have forgotten that in order to answer the scientific question we must act, and that the choice of the form of action which gives us science is a choice, not an inescapable necessity. We must act before we can know; we must act in order to know; and the decision to act scientifically constitutes one way of answering the general religious question by saying, "I shall respond scientifically; I shall be a scientific kind of person." The religious question, therefore, necessarily encloses and sustains any scientific form of question and answer. Science is not self-creating. We create science by choosing to respond to the world about us in a certain way. However radically we may modify our future action by what we find out, the priority of personal action remains fundamental. Thus science is not the test by which religion is validated. On the contrary, science itself can be considered a species of religious response, although it is the not same religious response that biblical religion is.

The final resolution of the relation between science and biblical religion will turn on the necessity for accepting our personal participation in and responsibility for our knowledge. We create our knowledge by interacting with the world, and we cannot so separate ourselves from our world that we can precisely define or delimit either ourselves in abstraction from the world, or the world in abstraction from ourselves. What we know is always a function of how we have chosen to act in order to know. Our knowledge and our existence contain an ineradicable dialectic expressed specifically, but not exclusively, by a permanent tension between science and biblical religion.

In the dialectic between biblical religion and science, each functions as a limit upon the other. Science prevents us from inventing and attempting to live within a fantasy world—and one of these fantasies may be the notion of God and his action in history. Biblical religion, by reminding us of who we are, keeps us from forgetting that we are responsible for the creation of knowledge since the criteria by which we test both scientific and religious truth claims are those we have chosen to use. Thus the dilemma of knowledge and the dialectic of truth is that we must look both ways at once, and every truth judgment about experience must be a tentative one because of this dialectic.

The same dialectic appears also in our language, because through it the person speaks of the world he knows. Necessarily, all language, both religious and scientific, is at best paradoxical and mythical, an image of reality rather than a flat, precise, factual account. In the end, the problem of the relation of religion and science is the dual problem of discerning and of accepting with humility the ambiguous state of our existence, from which neither scientific knowledge nor a revelation from God procures our release.

The publication of this book brings to concrete fruition the stimulus I received from attendance at two faculty conferences on science and religion, sponsored by the Danforth Foundation at Pennsylvania State University during the summers of 1956 and 1957 and directed by Dean Harold K. Schilling and Dr. Luther Harshbarger, and from a year's study at the University of Manchester with Professors Dorothy Emmet and Michael Polanyi. I wish also to thank the administration of Iowa State University of Science and Technology who arranged a reduced teaching load which enabled me to complete the writing of the book.

My special thanks for encouragement and enlightenment must go to a group of Iowa State University colleagues organized by Walter R. Rothenbuhler, then Professor of Zoology and now at Ohio State University. The other members of the group were Ellis H. Hicks and Martin J. Ulmer, Professors of Zoology, Gordon C. Danielson, Professor of Physics, John C. Greene, Professor of History of Science, now at the University of Kansas, Donald R. Benson, Associate Professor of English, and my wife. Weekly, for more than two years, we met at luncheon to discuss the relationships between science and religion for our edification—and to the amazement of our colleagues who overheard our frequently heated debates. Preliminary drafts of these chapters provided the basis for many of our discussions. I learned more from these sessions than I contributed to them, and I have appropriated gratefully and without credit what they taught me. My failure to give my colleagues proper footnote citations is justified only by the fact that they will recognize here very little of what they said in reply to what I first wrote. Their lack of success in saving me from innumerable errors in statement and in understanding should be a salutary warning to those who are bemused by the legendary power of education to solve all problems.

Two dear friends have given me highly valued editorial assistance: the editorial encouragement of the late Kathryn Benbrook Lapp rescued this project when it was grounded by foggy language; Rowena James has edited the manuscript for the Iowa State University Press. Mary McDermott Shideler, who honors me by being my wife, detected fuzziness in many sentences that I had thought were perfectly clear, and her sensitivity to style has vastly improved my own. The infelicities which remain are here because I overruled their judgments.

The epigraphs, except that for Chapter Seven, are taken from the text of the Revised Standard Version of the Bible, copyright by the National Council of Churches of Christ in the United States of America; the epigraph for Chapter Seven is taken from the text of the New English Bible, copyright by Oxford University Press and Cambridge University Press.

EMERSON W. SHIDELER
Iowa State University
Ames, Iowa

Part One ✹

THE CONTOURS OF THE PROBLEM

Chapter One

THE NEW WARFARE BETWEEN SCIENCE AND THEOLOGY

They have healed the wound of my people lightly, saying, "Peace, peace," when there is no peace. JEREMIAH 6:14

THE ILLUSION OF PEACE

OUR WESTERN CULTURE has rightly been called scientific. The attitudes and goals of science are the common possession of us all. While only a few of us are professional scientists, scientific ways of thinking are part of our mental furniture; directly and indirectly we provide great sums for scientific research; we all enjoy the fruits of scientific technology; and specific training in science is considered an essential part of every educational program.

Our culture is also religious, and not merely in the sense of an external religiosity. An authentic theological revival, centering in the rediscovery of the Bible, now stirs both Protestant and Roman Catholic churches and arouses the interest of great numbers of people who have no specific ecclesiastical commitments. The affairs of churches are important news. Secular journals of opinion publish essays by theologians, and religious books have a ready sale. There is widespread interest in theological questions, although we are far from the situation of the sixteenth and seventeenth centuries when laymen conducted informed theological discussions and kings wrote theological treatises.

However, the mood of laymen today when they discuss theological questions is one of puzzlement and embarrassment rather than of the confident exposition of well-considered judgments. Their perplexity with theology comes from causes that are more fundamental than religious illiteracy, great as this may be even in the midst of our renewed interest in religious matters. It arises directly from our scientific ways of thought. And this confusion of understanding does not simply mark the distance between the prescientific age of the Bible and our own. The barrier lies in the fact that our scientific ways of thought are not those of biblical religion.

Whether or not our society is split into two cultures, the humanistic and the scientific, as many people are saying, the gears do not mesh when we shift from scientific ways of thought to biblical ways of thinking. The clash is particularly obvious when professional theologians and scientists attempt to talk, but it appears in all of us when we try to be both scientific and religious in the manner of the revived biblical theology. In this clash, an old problem, which many people have dismissed today as solved, has returned. What had appeared to be peace between science and religion has turned out to be only a temporary truce. Peace has not been declared between science and the biblical faith.

In many quarters, the traditional struggle over

the old issues still goes on in the old language. Some scientists still identify Christianity and the Bible as their chief enemy. And, periodically, Christian groups confirm this enmity by attacking "godless science" or by attempting to suppress the teaching of evolution in the schools. Such vestigial skirmishes can be dismissed as irrelevant. Like soldiers who have not heard the news of surrender, these combatants on both sides continue a battle long since finished. They are trapped in the stereotypes of previous generations. The news of the significant changes which have occurred in both religion and science has not penetrated to their remote sectors of the ideological jungle. But their instinct is correct. They sense an authentic issue, however unenlightened and misguided their attacks on each other may be, and despite their failure to identify it or illuminate it.

The illusion of peace between science and biblical faith is in great part a product of the success of liberal theology in accommodating biblical religion to science. But the success of liberalism has been too great. The integrity of biblical religion has been submerged by scientific criteria of judgment, which meant that Christian claims could be allowed to stand only if they were scientifically legitimate. Theological liberalism has made enormous contributions to our understanding of the life and times and ways of thought of the biblical tradition and of Christian history. But in the process, religious issues have been transmuted into cultural and historical problems. The chief questions became those of cultural history which could be answered by the methods of scientific research. It was as if by clarifying the cultural history of the Hebrews, we could decide whether and how seriously we should take their understanding of the covenant relationship between

God and man. It was as if by determining the authentic biblical text and by answering the questions of authorship and circumstances of writing, we were to confront the Word of God.

By using liberalism's scientific methods of biblical study, the creation stories were identified as primitive folklore, and the fairly obvious resemblances between Babylonian creation myths and the first chapter of Genesis accounted for the biblical form of the creation story. The historical Jesus was distinguished from the Christ of the early Christian community's faith by applying principles of analysis learned from the scientific study of culture, language, and literature. Evolution was made the clue to history as well as to biology, and by using it, the primitive stages of biblical religious faith could be identified and dismissed. The religion of the Bible tended to be interpreted as only one cultural tradition among many, all of which reflected the parochialism of their environments, so that the biblical tradition had no inherent claim to superiority over the other great Eastern religions, and was perhaps destined to be surpassed as men advanced in scientific knowledge.

Theological liberalism has taught us that the Word of God is spoken in human words and that the water of life is carried in earthen vessels. This is a salutary corrective to the tendency to identify the words of the Bible as the Word*s* of God, and thus to lose man's participation in the revelatory process. But in the terms of the liberal position, the Word of God could no longer be distinguished from the words of men who spoke in specific cultural situations which no longer exist. Theological liberalism had no message to speak which was different from the gospel of the sciences: natural, biological, and behavioral. It only promised the triumph of man's innate goodness, guided by his intelligence, which was exhibited by the power of science to destroy pockets of ignorance.

This liberal accommodation of the Christian message to science has come unstuck. Biblical theology, under a variety of labels, has arisen in reaction to liberalism's loss of any authentic biblical message. But this return to the Bible is not a fundamentalistic literalism. Therefore, those who still battle evolution in the name of the Bible have misplaced the emphasis and are fighting for a lost cause.

The newer biblical theology recognizes the human character of the Bible. It accepts the results of the scientific study of these records, and of the culture, the environment, and the thought forms of the Bible and the Christian tradition. But these data do not authenticate the Bible's message. However richly they illuminate the environment of the biblical revelation, they do not constitute the revelation. The biblical message has its own integrity, and contemporary biblical theologians speak from the confidence generated by this independence of the biblical message. The authenticity of God's confrontation through the Bible does not depend upon any scientific verification or confirmation. Indeed, such verification is not possible so far as biblical theology is concerned. Scientific knowledge about biblical religion is a way station on the road to truth, not the destination. Such scientific knowledge may be immeasurably valuable, but it represents a different concern from that of biblical religion.

There is a penetrating irony in the collapse of liberalism among theologians. Many lay people—among them professional scientists—are now discovering, a generation late, the fruits of scientific scholarship in religion. They now urge liberalism's accommodation of science and Christianity as a way of removing conflict and preserving the values of religious faith. In this vein they write "new" theologies which point to a scientific fulfillment of the Kingdom of God.[1] The irony of such efforts lies not only in the naive failure of these apologists to perceive what biblical theologians now emphasize, namely the legitimate distinctiveness of science from religion; it also marks the significant failure of the churches to keep laymen abreast of theological advances. In a different way, this kind of outmoded liberalism among laymen reveals the breadth of the gap in understanding between scientific and theological ways of thinking.

Science and biblical religion are not the same activities, and studies from both sides emphasize their distinctiveness. Recent work has not brought them closer together but has pushed them farther apart to the point where a different kind of illusion of peace has developed. The two fields have become so isolated because of the specialization of knowledge that the implications of one for the other have been lost. On the one hand, the awareness of the integrity of biblical theology in its own terms enables theologians to pursue their studies without regard to the direction scientific research takes. On the other hand, scientific research, particularly in the physical sciences, has so fragmented into specialized studies that communication among scientists has itself become a branch of technical research, and it threatens to develop into a speciality in its own right as computer indexing of scientific litera-

[1] Cf. Harlow Shapley, ed., *Science Ponders Religion* (New York: Appleton-Century-Crofts, 1960). Cf. Edwin P. Booth, ed., *Religion Ponders Science* (New York: Appleton-Century-Crofts, 1964), for a reply from a conservative, if not fundamentalist, theological position.

ture increases. This fragmentation of knowledge sustains the kind of peace that rests merely upon simple ignorance of what the other is doing.

In the current separation of science from biblical religion, two avenues of possible contact can be discerned. One is a growing theological concern for nature, particularly in terms of the doctrine of creation, although it is not yet apparent what theologians can say that will be relevant for scientific work. The other avenue consists of the studies of man that are being carried on by the behavioral sciences. As these sciences succeed in embracing more and more of man's social and private life, from his sexual activities to his political organizations, the clash between the biblical view of man and the scientific view of man will become apparent to everyone. When this happens we may well see a repetition of the battle over evolution which occurred, in part at least, because everybody could see the implications of evolutionary theory for certain cherished notions about origins. Similarly, the behavioral sciences are now threatening the Christian view of man. Defenders of Christianity will be tempted to reply by denying that the findings of the behavioral sciences are accurate, as an earlier generation attacked the accuracy of evolutionary biologists. If this misguided defense is made, the mistaken champions of Christianity will repeat the battle which was lost against Copernicus, Galileo, Darwin, and Freud. We will have again confused content with function.

One plausible guard against the confusion of content with function and among functions seems to be by accepting the popular notion that science and religion have different objects of concern: science deals with nature while religion deals with God. (This is one implication of the word theology: the *logos* or science of God.) On this basis, religion would have nothing to do with our immediate problems, and spokesmen for the church should abstain from comment about politics or social problems and confine themselves strictly to God, salvation, and the future life. In a trivial sense, one would then talk religiously whenever he dragged God into the conversation, as political orators are so fond of doing. By the same token, all discussion of our experienced world, natural and social, would belong to science. Our daily life would be exclusively the sphere of science and other nonreligious human activities, and biblical religion would be irrelevant to these. If this position were taken, the two fields would not collide because they would no longer meet, and an essential biblical claim would be denied.

According to the Bible, God is the God of history. He is the God who declares himself in the concrete history of man, and he created the world of nature to be the theater of man's history. Whether this claim is true or false is the problem of the truth of biblical religion. But whether true or false, the fact that it is made at all implies that biblical religion concerns itself with the same world of experience as that which science studies. The originally promising and facile distinction between objects of concern or of content has collapsed. We are now aware that both biblical religion and science refer to the same world of experience, and this confronts us with a dilemma.

To state this dilemma in another form: when the same separation between the concerns of science and those of religion is employed to deal with the problem of historical and scientific inaccuracies in the Bible itself, one is then tempted to say that the Bible is a book of religion, not science. Its religious message is the important thing, and the primitive prescientific views one finds there are to be ignored in favor of our own much better science. Insofar as the biblical message has been identified with these prescientific views, they must be abandoned in order for the biblical message to be heard.[2] Likewise, the Bible's religious message should not be tied to the correctness of its historical narrative. Perhaps the Hebrews were not actually descendants of a single ancestor, as the biblical narrative suggests. Perhaps Abraham, Isaac, and Jacob were not father, son, and grandson, but leaders of separate clans which finally amalgamated in Palestine to form the Hebrew people. It seems most unlikely that the entire nation was in Egypt or that the whole people was present at Mt. Sinai. The chronology of the Hebrew kings appears to be fairly secure, but the date of the Exodus from Egypt and the occupation of the land of Canaan is in dispute. It is probable that Moses lived, but if so, we know little else about him, and the story of Moses on Mt. Sinai is hardly a faultless report of his conversations with Yahweh. In fact, biblical scholars have not been able to agree on the location of the sacred mountain. Similar historical doubts assail the New Testament records of Jesus and the apostles.

The fact remains that the content of the biblical message dissolves when its anchorage in history is cut, and it then becomes another timeless cosmic drama in the style of Buddhism and the mystery cults of the New Testament period. God is not the God of history if there is no history for him to be God of. So again the

[2] This is the program of Demythologizing urged by Rudolph Bultmann in his essay, "New Testament and Mythology," in Hans Werner Bartsch, ed., *Kerygma and Myth: A Theological Debate,* trans. Reginald H. Fuller (London: S.P.C.K., 1957), pp. 1–44.

concerns of biblical religious faith and those of scientific research intersect in the world of ordinary experience. The claim of biblical religion to be a historical religion confronts us with the dilemma that both biblical religion and science talk about the same world.

Faced with this dilemma, the fundamentalist theologian has assumed that the immediacy of the Bible's message for today depends upon the accuracy of the Bible's reports of historical and scientific data. For him, therefore, any historical research which attacks the accuracy of any of the Bible's data both destroys the biblical message and denies its relevance for today by pushing the Bible back into the remote past. Because he equates the Bible's message with its reported data, the fundamentalist has been forced into the disastrous error of defending the Bible from all criticism, including that of scientific evidence. Equally fundamentalist scientists have made the same erroneous equation, but in reverse, by assuming that when they have refuted the Bible's data, they have succeeded in annulling the Bible's religion. Either way, the dilemma is rejected by denying, on the one hand, the relevance of science, or on the other hand, the relevance of the Bible for our world of experience.

The theological liberal's mistaken resolution of the same dilemma has been to assume that the human and natural story of the past constituted the biblical message, so that recovering an accurate history of man and nature was to preach the Gospel. Thus he made scientific categories sovereign, because science is the way we get accurate information about the world, past and present.

However, the issue is much more subtle and complicated than these simplistic formulations would suggest. The resurgence of biblical theology has revived the warfare between science and theology by affirming in unmistakable fashion both the necessity for scientific information and the integrity of the Bible's religion in its own terms.

THE BATTLE OF WORDS

MUCH of the contemporary discussion of the issues between science and religion has shifted its ground from the problem of content and rival claims to the language problem. The discussion now turns on the nature of the language being used rather than, as in the past, upon the choice between rival claims.

Two factors have prompted this shift of ground in the debate. One is the nature of the problems that arise when the verification criterion which is applicable to scientific language is applied also to religious language. The other is the recognition that language has many functions, and that confusion comes from failing to distinguish between the functions of scientific language and those of religious language. These two factors reinforce each other. The realization that language has many functions has developed out of the difficulties that philosophers of language have uncovered in the verification of religious statements. The verification criterion sets the task of specifying the conditions for truth. It is the question of identifying precisely the conditions or circumstances which must be fulfilled in order for a statement to be recognized as true. In its more recent form, the verification issue has been stated negatively, as a falsification criterion, because it is logically simpler to specify the conditions under which a statement would be false than to specify the conditions for its truth.

These conditions can be precisely designated for

scientific statements. The scientist knows how to read or interpret his data exactly because he has already decided what conditions would confirm or would refute his hypothesis. He can design an effective experiment because he knows what he is looking for. This does not mean that he knows in advance what the answer will be, but that he does know what will constitute an answer, and he knows how to identify an answer because he has set down the conditions to be satisfied.

In these terms science has moved along two fronts. One has been a constant expansion of the fund of information about the behavior of the natural world. The other, and more important, has been the refinement of methodology, particularly in the physical sciences, by increasing the specificity of the questions being asked, and the precision in defining what will serve as an answer.

The methodology of the behavioral sciences has not yet caught up with the fund of information. It is much less clear in sociology than in physics when a question has been answered, or what would be accepted as an answer. Complex as nuclear fusion may be, it is much easier to decide whether and how it has occurred than to decide whether a marriage is happy. Behavioral scientists are engaged in extensive study of such issues, but they do not yet agree on the conditions which identify a happy marriage—or the conditions which constitute an unhappy one. They have not agreed on what counts as evidence to answer the question.

In religion the situation is still more confused. It is only recently that the verification problem has been raised in a significant form. Theologians have not often faced the query of what conditions or events they would accept as making their assertions false.[3] For example, one of the great historical debates has been over the problems of evil and suffering, because their occurrence has been proposed as a challenge to the claim that God is good and loving. Theologians have replied that these conditions do not at all contradict the claim that God is good. Various explanations or reconciliations have been offered, perhaps the frankest one being the explanation employed in certain portions of the Bible itself, especially by the Deuteronomic historian, that evil and suffering are punishment and these people get just what they deserve. Some statements from Jesus reject this idea, as does the Book of Job. Whatever the answer, the intention remains the same: to show that there is no contradiction between the given circumstances and God's goodness or omnipotence or benevolence or wisdom or whatever other characteristic has been challenged.

For our purpose, the issue in the illustration is not whether one given explanation of evil or suffering is better or more adequate than some other, but the implication of such attempts at explanation, because this injects the falsification or verification of religious statements into the discussion. Are there circumstances or conditions which, for example, would represent the absence of God's love, or the falsity of the statement that God is love?[4] Many theologians seem to take the position that such religious statements are true in the face of

[3] Jeremiah suggests the criterion he would accept in his controversy with Hananiah over the question of whose prophecy was true, Jer. 28:9.

[4] Cf. Antony Flew and Alasdair Macintyre, eds., *New Essays in Philosophical Theology* (London: SCM Press, 1955), pp. 95–130.

all possible circumstances, and that no situation or condition would make such statements false.

The same issue arises for many other assertions that are central to the Christian faith. The classic creeds—Apostles', Nicene, and Athanasian—all consist of a series of assertions presumed to be true. The fact that each creed is prefaced by the phrase "I believe" does not alter the problem of determining what would confirm belief, or would justify abandoning a belief as false. In some cases, we can indicate the kind of data or circumstances that would be accepted as evidence of the falsity of certain creedal propositions. For example, it is easy to identify the kind of historical evidence which would show that some other procurator than Pilate ruled in Jerusalem at the time of the crucifixion of Jesus, and to specify the kind of biological data which would be required to show that the conception and birth of Jesus were entirely normal.

The issue here must not be misconstrued. We are not concerned with the likelihood that such evidence would turn up. The issue instead, is the kind of evidence we would accept. For, unless we can identify what we would accept as evidence, we have no way of knowing when we have found it.

The problem is acute with such statements as "Jesus is the only begotten Son of God," or "one God in three Persons," or "one Christ, very God, and very Man," or "of one substance with the Father," or "God was in Christ reconciling the world unto himself." With respect to these, what would count as evidence one way or the other is not at all clear. When the creeds declare God to be "Maker of heaven and earth," no evidence that would falsify such a claim can be conceived. And while it is comparatively easy to show what philosophical issues led to some of these formulas, that historical investigation in itself does not establish their truth.

Statements like these, which either are compatible with all situations or which cannot be confirmed at all, raise the serious question of what meaning the term "true" can carry when it is applied to them. The problem simply is that these religious statements and others like them cannot meet the verification standard of scientific statements. Therefore, religious statements cannot be called "true" in the sense that scientific statements are called "true." One obvious alternative, of course, would be that religious statements are false. However, if by the verification principle they are not true, neither are they false. The conclusion seems to be then, that the term "true" does not fit at all, because religious statements do not have any content to which the terms "true" or "false" can be applied.

The term "true," as used by those who urge the verification criterion, applies only to statements which convey knowledge, and only those statements convey knowledge which distinguish between different situations or events. Clearly, scientific language fits this qualification. Scientific statements tell us something about events by distinguishing between differing situations, and thus they can be certified as true or false. On the other hand, a statement which is compatible with all situations conveys no knowledge because it fails to make any distinction between differing conditions. On these terms, the statement "God loves me" conveys no information if it is said to be "true" regardless of what happens to me. What we want to know is whether God loves us or not—what the difference is between the situation "God loves us," and the situation "God does not love us," and how we can tell which situation is the case. If every situation, without qualification, is an example of God's love, then God's love makes no distinction between one situation and any other. To "know," then, that God loves us, tells us exactly nothing about our experience because no distinctions between situations have been identified by this assertion. The statement adds nothing to our knowledge of what the world is or how our experience proceeds, precisely because it leaves everything just as it was before. Nothing would be changed if the statement were to be abandoned, because all things would remain the same. If this example seems to be another instance of asking the wrong question, this impression confirms the main point, namely, that such statements do not convey knowledge, but perform some entirely different function.

At this point most Christians are likely to recoil, feeling that a very great deal is lost by abandoning such a statement as "God loves us." But what is it that would be lost or be changed?—inquire those who urge the verification principle. And when the Christian tries to answer this question, he will almost certainly find himself in trouble. If he gives a specific answer which identifies some situation of suffering or tragedy as an instance of the absence or withdrawal of God's love, he satisfies the verification criterion. But he denies what Christians have traditionally said about God. If he states what Christians have traditionally taught about the universality and never failing constancy of God's love, then he makes a statement which fails to tell us anything about the world or our experience, because it fails to distinguish between situations. His statement would convey no knowledge, and this contradicts the Christian's claim that such statements do convey knowledge.

Since religious language seems not to be cognitive

in the way scientific language is, the question has shifted to the function and meaning religious language does have. It is now recognized that the meaningfulness of a statement must be identified in terms of language use, and is not to be restricted, as Ayer originally proposed, to references to direct sensory experience.[5] What a sentence means depends upon how it is used, what function it serves in communication. Language has many functions in addition to that of recording the data of experience, as Wittgenstein has pointed out.[6] The commands to close the door or to halt at a through street, are perfectly meaningful statements, although they convey no knowledge content at all. The term "language-game" was introduced by Wittgenstein[7] both to identify this variety of language function, and "to bring into prominence the fact that the *speaking* of language is part of an activity, or of a form of life." [8] He was emphasizing the important fact that language is a tool for communication, used according to rules which vary from one situation and intention to another, as the rules for games vary. There is no single or uniform or absolutely proper language. No word or sentence has a universal and intrinsic meaning; its meaning comes from its use. In order to know what a sentence means one must identify what the speaker is doing, what game he is playing with his words. While the term "language-game" has tended to become a cliché, the insight it offers has been of great assistance in clarifying the problem. It emphasizes something that still has not been realized

[5] Alfred Jules Ayer, *Language, Truth and Logic* (New York: Dover Publications, 1952), Chapter I, pp. 33–45; cf. pp. 11–16 in his new Introduction to this reprint edition.

[6] Ludwig Wittgenstein, *Philosophical Investigations*, trans. G. E. M. Anscombe (New York: Macmillan, 1953), pp. 11–12.

[7] *Ibid.*, p. 5.

[8] *Ibid.*, p. 11.

widely or deeply enough: that language is a form of action, a pattern for behavior, a way of seizing upon and organizing experience, and not simply a collection of counters, so that knowledge is a creation and not just a store of data.

Philosophers have suggested a variety of functions for the language of Christian faith. There is Ayer's emotive classification:[9] he maintains that through religious, metaphysical, and ethical language, we express our emotions or attitudes, and all that this kind of speech tells us is something about the attitudes of those who use it. To call something good, for example, says nothing about that object, but only indicates the speaker's approval of it.

R. B. Braithewaite[10] has argued that empirical evidence shows religious language to be a policy language. Statements of belief are actually proclamations of the moral policies we propose to follow. To say that God is love really means that we propose to make love our moral guide. Such a statement does not say anything about God himself. According to Braithewaite, much of the vocabulary of religious speech is in the form of myths, such as the stories about Jesus, and are not to be taken as history. Their function is not to record certain historical data, but to dramatize the moral judgments we make. And their effectiveness in portraying the moral policies we advocate does not depend upon their accuracy as historical accounts.

Ian Ramsey[11] warns that religious language has an odd logical character, despite its similarity to other

[9] Ayer, Chapter VI, pp. 102–120.

[10] R. B. Braithewaite, *An Empiricist's View of the Nature of Religious Belief* (Cambridge: The University Press, 1955).

[11] Ian T. Ramsey, *Religious Language* (London: SCM Press, 1957).

kinds of language. Scientific language has a familiar structure or logic, and religious sentences apparently follow the same form. But this appearance is deceptive since religious sentences have a different inner logic which is not compatible with our ordinary logical analysis. A sentence about God grammatically resembles a sentence about a potato. But since our relation to God is not similar to our relation to potatoes, the two sentences cannot have the same inner logic. Since in religion we are forced to use language derived from ordinary experience, we must be continually aware of this odd logic in our religious sentences. Religious sentences suggest and point, while scientific sentences precisely characterize. The most that one can hope for from religious language is that his hearer will catch on "when the penny drops," in contrast to the precise identification given in scientific language.

Willem Zuurdeeg[12] has urged that religious language be understood as convictional language, for language is the way we declare ourselves and grasp our world. Man's fundamental characteristic is that he has convictions or commitments, and he proclaims these by his speaking. The convictional character of religious language inheres in the action of speaking itself, as expression and communication of the person who thus proclaims how he will appropriate his world. He does not speak simply from within himself, but in response to something which has grasped him, convicted him, and his words point to this convictor. But his words are not to be taken as a flat and neutral account of that entity, and they would say little to one who had not been similarly convicted. The meaning lies in the

[12] Willem Zuurdeeg, *An Analytical Philosophy of Religion* (New York: Abingdon, 1958).

person acting in his speech, rather than in the words he uses.

By shifting attention away from the content of sentences to the function the sentences perform, these analyses, in particular that of Zuurdeeg, point toward a solution of the problem. What goes on in religious language is different from what goes on in scientific language. Such a statement as "God is omnipotent," or "God was in Christ reconciling the world unto himself," does not carry the same *kind* of meaning as "Water decomposes into two gases in a volume ratio of two to one." And these differing statements are not verified in the same way. If we persist in dealing with the statements from religion in the same terms as we deal with those from science, we only continue the confusions of the past. Language analysis has now shown that this corridor has no exit, and that we misrepresent the content of both religion and science if we fail to take full account of the differing functions which produced them. Language analysis now points us away from this error which still persists among the linguistically unsophisticated among both scientists and theologians.

Both philosophers of language and theologians who take language analysis seriously are agreed that in terms of its own "game," religious language is authentically meaningful, and not—as early critiques had it—meaningless. However, this may be a Pyrrhic victory. The meaningfulness which these analyses allow to religious language continues to deny to it the knowledge content that Christians have always believed they were communicating. The problem of relating religious language to scientific language has not been solved, but has instead been falsely dissolved by severing the two fields and their functions completely. These analyses merely return the discussion to the level where there is no occasion for conflict because, by confining knowledge statements to scientific language, science and religion no longer deal with any common realm of experience.

This price for peace is too high. These language analyses purport to be complete accounts of what religious language means and does, but the functions they assign to religious language do not fully capture what Christians think they are doing. By sharply separating religious language from other kinds of speech, these analyses assign to religious language precise and limited functions which fail to encompass the full range of religious phenomena and activity. The fact that several differing and mutually exclusive functions have been identified indicates that more is going on than studies such as these have identified. Religious language does fulfill these functions. But since it fulfills all of them and more, the analyses misrepresent religious activity by confining it too narrowly. They are not therefore mistaken, but they are insufficient for the job.

Further, it must be said that such analyses as these perpetuate a faulty concept of what knowledge is, because they share the common assumption that there is a clear separation between the knowing person and the world he knows. Knowledge, therefore, has been taken to be an independent body of data about that external world. The presupposition is that since this world is external to, and clearly distinct from, the person who knows it, it will be the same world for all persons, and knowledge of that world should be uniform for all persons. Any given individual can check his own perception by comparing it with another person's, because they have the same access to the same world. And the verification or falsification criterion formalizes this process of comparison. Science is presumed to be this kind of uniform knowledge about that external world.

In these terms, if religion also provides knowledge, then it should be possible to confirm these religious claims in the same fashion that we confirm scientific claims. But we now know that religious claims cannot be so verified. From this situation, and guided by this faulty view of knowledge, linguistic philosophers have drawn the mistaken conclusion that religious language conveys no knowledge content.

The error lies in amputating the person from his knowledge, so that it becomes something he collects from the world and God rather than something he creates in his interaction with the world or with God. If knowledge is created in interaction, then the kind of action the person takes and the kind of question he asks play a powerful role in determining the shape and content of his knowledge. It is not enough to compare final contents or results, as if the actions and relationships and questions which produced them were identical. It is not enough to compare the language forms in which the contents are stated. It is certainly an advance to recognize that different activities do underlie differing languages. But the primary question is not touched by attending simply to language itself.

The first issue is: What are men doing when they interact with the world scientifically, as compared with what they are doing when they interact with the world religiously and Christianly? Science and the Christian form of religion represent different modes of human action. They arise in different interactions between man and his world of experience. These differing interactions represent differing fundamental questions which men ask about themselves and the world. The relationship between science and religion depends finally upon the nature of these questions, and upon the function of these questions within the life of man.

Chapter Two ✱

THE INITIAL QUESTION

Then the Lord answered Job out of the whirlwind: "Who is this that darkens counsel by words without knowledge? Gird up your loins like a man, I will question you, and you shall declare to me."

JOB 38:1–3

ANSWERS WITHOUT QUESTIONS

SCIENCE AND RELIGION are ways by which we cope with our experience, ways by which we relate ourselves to whatever confronts us. They are forms of action which we employ to guide our interaction with whatever surrounds us. They are patterns of relationship by which we participate in whatever is going on. Each charts a quest for meaning.

Because science and religion have stood before us as great structures of secure knowledge, we have not often seen that both are activities. They have weighed us down as huge masses of material to be mastered, instead of presenting us with alternative forms of participation. The life of the undergraduate student (and frequently that of the postdoctoral research fellow also) has become a desperate struggle to catch up with the accumulation of information so that he can take his place in the laboratory, while the student of religion is inundated by the variety and subtlety of the views he is expected to be versed in. It is little wonder that the inexpert layman, despairing of bringing that diversity in either field under control, dismisses the judgments of the expert as mere opinion, while at the same time he clings tightly to his own opinion as the only truth he needs.

Apart from the moralism of "good works," the nature of religious activity has been, to the ordinary person, even more inscrutable than the activities going on behind the locked doors of scientific laboratories engaged in classified research. Religion has commonly been interpreted as a complete and final set of claims to be affirmed without alteration or debate, and religiousness has been identified with church attendance and conformity to the conventional moral code the church advocates. Morality is almost the only religious activity most people identify, so that it is quite acceptable for one to say that his religion is the Golden Rule. We do attempt to train workers in science, but comparable training in religious functions has been relegated to the cloister, or waits upon the mystery of a "call." The results of the search for truth have been taught but not the process of the seeking. The destination has been described without charting the pattern of the journey.

Both science and religion must be seen primarily as activities, not as completed contents, and they are different activities because they originate in different questions. But since we have not seen those initiating questions, we have failed to discern the fundamental differences between science and religion. We have compared and contrasted them as if they were cut from the same cloth. The questions are different, not because they are addressed to different objects, but because their primary concern is different. They seek different goals and represent different purposes.

THE SCIENTIFIC QUESTION

SCIENCE, as suggested in the Introduction, originates in the question, "What is that?"—a question which occurs in a number of forms such as: "What is happening?" "What is the world?" "What is man?" "What is the nature of things?" Whatever the exact style the question takes, when we raise it we are asking what the world outside us is, what confronts us, what is the source of our experience. Naturally and justifiably, we assume that we are surrounded by a multitude of things and events which do not have their source in us, and we want to know what these things are. In a legitimate sense, science begins in curiosity. We want to know what is going on around us, and we are developing techniques to explore every form of experience from voting behavior to the processes which sustain the stars.

Whenever we attempt to define or to identify or to describe any thing or event in our experience, we are answering the question that generates science. Science is not, therefore, a fairly recent development in the history of man, for man has always been asking and answering this question. What is new is how vastly we have increased our technical skill in getting answers to our question, an increase which is a direct consequence of our dominating assumption that the most important question we face is the query, "What?" Our culture has been made a scientific culture by our tacit agreement that what we need most is more and better information about the world around us. To give only one example, there is substantial significance in the frequency with which we greet proposals for action by replying that first we need more research.

But, despite our success in research, science is not simply the information we thus accumulate, and the meaning of the question which initiates science does not lie simply in the answers it gives us. The meaning lies in the kind of activity the scientific question generates, and that activity consists in the specific kind of relationship that we adopt toward what we observe and describe. Scientific activity directs attention away from one's self and toward the source of experience. It removes the self as far as possible from the situation so that the situation can disclose its nature uninfluenced (again, as far as possible) by the presence of the observer.

The defining characteristic of scientific activity is this focus of attention upon the world as it exists independently of those who observe it. To be a scientist is not, therefore, primarily to know something. Knowledge is the product, and possessing it is not the mark of a scientist. Instead, to be a scientist is to act within this special kind of relationship in which a clear separation between one's self and the observed world is maintained, so that one does not confuse or distort the phenomena by his own presence.

The question itself dictates this kind of separation of the person from the phenomenon he studies. We ask this question because we want to know what the world—or that piece of it under observation—really is, and we mean by "really is" what it is in itself: what are the qualities, characteristics, behavior, and potentialities which belong specifically to it, distinguishing it from other things or events or situations.

However, more is at stake here than simple description—or measurement, which is a refined form of description. This would give us no more than a heap of individual instances, each separated from the others by its specific peculiarities, with apparent resemblance providing the only pattern among them. Scientists, and those who deal with the world in the scientific way, have long believed that the clue to the nature of things involves something more fundamental than the surface peculiarities which distinguish individuals from each other. Earlier generations of scientists followed Aristotle in seeking that clue in some ultimate essence or essential nature of things, the substance of which things were made. Several important words in our present vocabulary, such as *element* and *atom,* as well as *substance* and *essence,* originated in the search for this underlying nature of things.

Modern scientists have abandoned the search for an essential or fundamental reality, and most of them, if not all, would resist the suggestion that *the* scientific question is the question of essences. Yet their objection would be another instance of the confusion between scientific activity and its specific results in a given period. In effect, the scientific question is still the question of the essence of things, what they really are in themselves, although no one now expects to find the answer in terms of some final and unchanging stuff whose qualities determine the flow of events and establish the nature of individual things. Perhaps the strangeness many scientists feel in the presence of theological talk comes from the fact that religion seems to offer in its realm just this kind of ultimate and unchanging substantial truth which scientists have long since discarded.

Scientists now talk in terms of functional interaction. They no longer consider things to be small chunks of some unchangeable substance, or entities with fixed characteristics belonging uniquely and permanently to each one. An event is no longer construed as a something in itself, capable of being characterized all by itself. Instead, any given thing is described as a function of specified changes occurring in other factors of the situation. An event is the interaction among these varying factors. Ideally, the pattern of interaction can be stated as a law in a formula which will enable one to calculate the changes to be expected in one factor when one is given the changes occurring in the others.

The search for a law stating a functional interaction among the factors in a situation does not represent a new kind of scientific question or activity; it does represent the conclusion that patterns can be found in events, and that these patterns give a clearer clue to what is going on than does a succession of discrete descriptions. That is, scientists have changed their notion of what constitutes an acceptable answer, but the question remains the same: they want to know as exactly and as fully as possible what kind of world we are involved in. Science is the activity we pursue to gain this account of what is going on.

This functional definition of science (which is itself, as a functional account, an instance of scientific activity), obviously extends the range of scientific activity beyond the conventional limits of the special sciences. My point is not to give the accolade of "scientific" to activities which do not deserve the label, but to identify an important question and its mode of action. Scientific activity is not necessarily confined to certain special programs. Whether a given program—for example, history—is a "science" or not depends upon one's judgment as to its success in answering the initial question. It may well be that history is a field of study where the factors are too numerous, too fluidly interconnected, and too uncertainly identified, to permit the dependability and precision we expect of a "science." But to make precision the definition of science as an activity is to perpetuate the old content errors, and to obscure the question underlying the activity. The historian or the puzzled householder with a blown fuse may not be able to answer their immediate questions with the precision a physicist can answer his. But they are asking the same kind of question: "What is going on?" And they want the same kind of answer: an account of events which tells them where they are in the stream of events, that is, an account which equips them to adjust their own behavior to what is going on.

This scientific question carries a correlative view of truth, or of what constitutes an acceptable answer (if one prefers not to use the term truth for scientific findings). Since the question is focussed upon the world and its events independently of the investigator, ideally his account should bear no mark of his own personal effect. The account should be the same regardless of who does the research or produces the statement. Variations between descriptions of the same situation, or the failure of other investigators to discover the same phenomenon, are taken as showing that someone has failed fully or correctly to attend to what is going on, or has permitted some influence of his own presence to affect his report. Truth, in the functional scientific sense, is the same for everyone, because it answers for every person the same question about the same object. Since that question is addressed to the world, not to the person himself, the answers are neutral and impartial with respect to persons.

The ideal of scientific impartiality does not carry any implication that scientific answers must be permanent and unchanging. Presumably, the world that is being studied is in a process of change; at least its parts seem to be changing as they interact. For this reason, the description or analysis of these changes will also vary as the processes of change proceed. But such changes in content are external to the investigators, and if their study is precise and correct, presumably they will produce a uniform account of the changes they observe.

The essence of scientific activity, then, is the neutral and detached relationship of the scientist with the world under study, so that its phenomena can be described in their own terms. The underlying assumption of the scientific question is that there is an independent phenomenon which has a nature or characteristics of its own. In order to discover it, the investigator must exclude himself as a functional participant in the situation, and this means detachment, neutrality, objectivity (in the common meaning of the word). The function of the investigator is to make the phenomenon speak for itself; he turns it into an object for his analysis. As subject he addresses his questions to an object, the world, and it is expected that if he does his job well, he will get the same answer as any other investigator.

THE RELIGIOUS QUESTION

THE question which begets religion usually appears in disguise, as if it were a matter of choosing between one religious tradition and another, or between some religion and none at all. In this form, religion seems to be an expendable option. Behind these superficial questions, however, there is the question of ultimate concern, the primordial and existential question which no man can escape and from which all religion flows. This is the elemental question, "Who am I?" or more generally, "Who are we?" As a preliminary, it must be carefully noted that this is *not* the scientific question, "What am I?" or more generally, "What is man?" which can be answered by the impartial accumulation of information about humanity as one type of being among others, or with some data about the family history or occupation or idiosyncrasies of a given individual. In every respect, the scientific question about man is no different from any other scientific question which inquires about the properties of some other nonhuman object or event.

Information in itself does not answer the religious question. Only action can answer it, for action *is* the answer. The answer to "Who?" is not a fact about the person; it is the person's declaration of himself, which he gives as he proclaims the being he chooses to be.

In its starkest form, the religious question finds the solitary individual in his aloneness facing his own actuality, and establishing his being as a self by his actions of initiation and response. Who he is depends upon who he wills to be. By these choices, he determines what self he will ultimately contribute to whatever relationships and interactions surround him, and, in turn, the form of his participation determines who he is.

One's choice of who he is does not depend upon the circumstances of his life, his inheritance of skills, or his means of livelihood, or the place and time of his birth. These are the given conditions within which he must act, and few of them are within the power of any of us to change, for birth plunges the person into a constellation of already existing hereditary and environmental forces. These environing circumstances will establish limits within which he can respond, but they do not establish how he will respond within his range of possibilities. Above all, they do not fix for him his declaration of himself—unless we arbitrarily deny all initiative to him by construing all human action as coerced reaction.

Initiative and responsibility for one's self by no means signify that one can, by willing it to be so, place himself in any position of power or security he desires, or invest himself with talents he has not been given. These conditions are fixed for him by his situation, but they are not his measure as a person, for who he is depends upon the meaning he seeks in his existence as he participates in, and contributes to, the relationships he is involved in.

There can be no question more ultimate than this religious question of the meaning of one's existence, because the person himself is addressed; he is the focus of concern. Such a concern is not egocentrism. Instead, here he faces his own responsibility for himself as the person he is within the circumstances given to him. He determines whether he will respond joyously or sullenly to events, whether he will contribute or seize with grasping hand, whether he will share in exchange or withdraw into the isolation which extinguishes him.

When one confronts himself at this level where religion begins, he discovers that the meaning of life is not given to him but is proclaimed by him; that the character of his existence is not received but declared; that his being is not a consequence of external operations but the originating power in which he acts to live.

Just as the understanding of science as an activity

pushes the boundaries of the scientific question far beyond the conventional sciences, so the understanding of religion, as that inner and primordial declaration of the self from which all else flows, pushes the boundaries of religion far beyond the traditional definitions. Such definitions conceal the fundamental action of the person by identifying religion with some institutional form, or by restricting it to some specified content, such as talk about God (in contrast to a science which talks about nature), or to private morals, or to speculation about the afterlife. This definition has instead a functional emphasis, as does Whitehead's "what one does with his solitariness," or Tillich's "questions of ultimate concern." It points to what one does.

In its most general existential sense, the religious question is inescapable, although it may not often be brought explicitly into focus. Every person must and does choose how he will act, even though the choice may be made unconsciously or by default, and in so choosing he declares his commitments. The question about religion is not, therefore, what is the difference between people who are not religious and those who are, for every person is religious in this fundamental sense. But religious commitment can take many different forms and be more or less central to the person's awareness and concern. Among these, biblical religion has its own special character, as a particular form of human response and declaration.

THE BIBLICAL QUESTION

MANY people would prefer to consider biblical religion, and Christianity specifically, as a God-given answer rather than as a question. And some contemporary theologians insist that Christianity should not be called a religion at all, for they say that religion is what man does, while Christianity is what God does. This objection both conceals and reveals the essential human response, the self declaration, which begets all religion, including that of the Bible. For whatever God does, biblical religion would be nothing at all without the response in which man declares himself.

The question initiating biblical religion occurs again and again in the biblical story: the covenant at Mt. Sinai, "All that the Lord has spoken we will do, and we will be obedient,"[1] Joshua's covenant at Shechem, "Choose this day whom you will serve," [2] the words of the prophet, "What does the Lord require of you?" [3] the words of Jesus, "No man can serve two masters," [4] "Seek first his kingdom," [5] and "If any man would come after me, let him deny himself and take up his cross daily and follow me." [6] The query is always the same: How do you respond to God?

In biblical religion, the general existential question becomes the specific demand for a personal response to a personal power. The biblical tradition declares that God, the source from which all existence comes, demands from man the response and responsibility of a person, rather than the reaction of a thing to external impacts. Christianity sharpens the question by declaring that by the Incarnation, God himself entered into and participated in the career of man to confront man with a Person whom man can accept or reject, but toward whom he cannot be neutral.

God is spoken of in personal terms in the Bible, not as a survival of primitive anthropomorphism, nor as a general proposition about divine beings, but as the

[1] Exodus 24:7.
[2] Joshua 24:15.
[3] Micah 6:8.
[4] Matthew 6:24.
[5] Matthew 6:33.
[6] Luke 9:23.

necessary expression of the biblical writers' experience that they were confronted with something—Someone—who compelled them to respond personally and responsibly. More precisely, they recognized themselves as persons because they were confronted by a Person. Isaiah's vision,[7] in which he saw himself more clearly than he saw God, was no mere reaction to a superior power, and he responded both by recognizing his own status in the presence of the Holy One of Israel, and by committing himself to the service of the One who had visited him. Jeremiah's anguish at the message he could neither stifle nor deliver without reaping scorn and persecution[8] was no mere neurotic indecision. He cried out in the agony of one who saw his duty given him by God, and courageously he willed to perform it, while facing the tragic consequences of what he did.

Whatever or whoever the God of the Bible is, he is that which demands this kind of personal response, and for whom only personal pronouns are appropriate. He requires his human creatures to be responsible persons in his presence, and he offers them a covenant with himself as the only relationship within which they can become the persons he created them to be. The essence of the personhood for which God created man, as the biblical writers understood it, requires that men take the responsibility for their own being in response to Another who also acts responsibly. The biblical writers thus use personal terms in speaking of God because God addresses them by demanding, "Who are you?" that is, "How do you respond to me?"

Christianity asks no different question. Indeed, by proclaiming the Christ as the one through whom God

[7] Isaiah 6:1–13.
[8] Jeremiah 15:10–18; 20:7–18.

acts to reconcile the world to himself, Christianity puts the religious question in terms that are more directly personal than those of the Old Testament. Christianity makes the question specific by receiving Christ as the Event to which men respond, as the Person to whom they declare themselves.

But the Christian question and its answering action in faith have been obscured. The direct issue of response to the Person of God's action has been permitted to become a debate about the precise nature of this Christ in whom God acts. The fundamental religious question has been concealed by disagreements about the mode of appropriate response, by variations in the form of celebration of the new relationship, and by differing organizational patterns within the community of believers.

Differing forms of Christian theology, worship, and organization reflect these differing understandings of how God acts and of how man should respond. Each form of Christianity constitutes a somewhat different way of being a person in response to God's action, so that the Christian religious question has tended to degenerate into a contest between competing forms of Christianity.

This diversity of understanding, and disagreement, about the acceptable response, exposes in full clarity the truth problem in religion. Just as the scientific kind of question carries a correlative definition of truth, so the religious question bears its related conception of truth. Because the religious question is the personal question, "Who are you?" the true answer must also be personal. Truth in religion is personal truth, that is, truth for persons in contrast to truth about things.

Truth becomes personal when it enables a person to recognize himself and declare himself. That is personal truth which authenticates and sustains the being persons have chosen as their own. It is that truth in which they recognize themselves made whole and fulfilled, in which their experiences find coherence and unity, in which their goals become radiant with value, in which their purposes are verified, and glory invests their being, in which they discover or are given joy and live abundantly. If such fruit comes rarely, perhaps it is because few people have known the fullness of truth for their own persons.

Religious truth in this sense is not primarily a concrete content; it does not consist essentially of a specific body of data to be distinguished from other bodies of data, or of a precisely formulated analysis of self or world set forth to correct other such analyses. It is not a collection of impartial statements about anything—self or world or objects—and would seem, therefore, to be empty. And it is empty if the only echoes we will accept from the term "truth" require that it consist in carefully discriminated bodies of content presenting an identical and interchangeable face to all observers.

Personal truth is not content but action; it is not statement but relationship. It is the knowing in one's acting that this is what he should do, that in this response he finds himself a whole being, that by participating in this relationship he knows himself an authentic person in community with other authentic persons. This is the kind of truth proclaimed by "For *I know* that my Redeemer lives,"[9] in contrast to a neutral demonstration that the redeemer is alive instead of dead. The "I know" is the cry of response of one who recognizes himself as being now rescued and healed, in contrast to a statement of the precise qualities or charac-

[9] Job 19:25, my italics.

teristics the savior must have in order to function in this capacity. Personal truth is the pattern of self-understanding within which the person responds to the world around him, within which he interprets his experience of that world, within which he lives and acts and knows himself.

Such truth is personal on two grounds. In one sense it is personal truth because it consists in, and requires the action of, a person who thereby declares himself by his participation. In it he gives himself, his own personal being, in the act of relationship. In the second sense, such truth is personal because in this relationship he discovers his being affirmed and verified, his goals lifted up and certified, and his meaning as a person supported and countersigned by a community of persons.

Part Two ✸

BIBLICAL RELIGION

Chapter Three ✸

THE BIBLICAL WORLD VIEW

By the word of the Lord the heavens were made,
and all their host by the breath of his mouth.
He gathered the waters of the sea as in a bottle;
he put the deeps in storehouses.
Let all the earth fear the Lord,
let all the inhabitants of the world stand in awe of him!
For he spoke, and it came to be;
he commanded, and it stood forth. PSALM 33:6–9

THE BIBLE'S WORLD AND OUR OWN

WHILE both religion and science are modes of action rather than commodities one possesses, the doing of either generates a content of practices, beliefs, institutions, interpretations of experience, and descriptions of the world and of human existence. And each produces as well a community of persons who hold this content as their common possession. By transmitting this content, new members are initiated into the life of the community, and by it the community's achievements and relationships are symbolized, recollected, and shared.

This content is used to test new insights; it provides the basis for judgments; it guides further exploration; and frequently enough, it functions as a limitation upon the range of further exploration.

In both science and biblical religion, this content is sufficiently massive and well established that mastery of it easily becomes a goal in itself, and in Christianity, all too often even this mastery of content has not been required for being enrolled as a member of the community. Applicants for membership in churches have been accepted if they could recite and give formal assent to a minimum list of doctrines, and conventional respectability has been taken as adequate participation in the community of faith. Similarly, many people in our culture have read something about science and claim to take "the scientific point of view." But mastery means effective participation as well as acquaintance with an accumulated content. One who has never actually worked in a laboratory can have only a small appreciation of what it means to be a scientist. Unless one has shared the struggle to find a meaningful way of asking an experimental question, has survived the frustration from equipment which refuses to cooperate, has reveled in the joy of discovery, and has responded to the beauty of an elegant demonstration, he is not yet a member of the scientific community. Likewise, one can be massively informed about the biblical tradition without having shared the life of the community of biblical faith. Simply to know about biblical religion or science is not enough to make one a fellow member of either community. But neither can one participate in either community if he is unacquainted with the results it has achieved or with the understanding of the world by which it gives meaning and direction to these results.

Most people are aware of the commonplace fact that the cosmology of the Bible is Ptolemaic, not Copernican. In the Bible, the earth is flat; it has boundaries and corners, and is roofed by the firmament through whose windows the rain pours to water the ground. The sun moves across the firmament to rule the day and give light upon the earth, and the moon rules the night. Above the firmament is heaven and hell is below the earth. The Lord ascended into heaven and he will return by coming down like a returning astronaut. However, no description of this cosmology can measure the distance between the biblical world view and that of our own day. The difference in cosmologies signalizes the difference in world views, but it does not capture it nor locate the essential points of contrast. In the Bible, events are seen in terms that are different from ours because they are interpreted by means of a different set of expectations about the kind of thing the world is and what will or will not happen in the world.

The primary difference appears in the initial questions themselves. The scientific question, "What?" not only separates the observer from the phenomena in a clear subject-object distinction, it also establishes a mechanical and quantitative relationship among events, because only this impersonal kind of description can be made uniform for all observers or be developed independently of any specific observer. The basic presumption of this scientific picture is that all events are to be understood as precisely identified reactions within a sequence of mensurable energy exchanges. Consciousness, will, purpose, personal response, are all to be dealt with as instances of quantitative energy exchanges.

By contrast, the biblical question, "How do you respond to God's creative and reconciling activity?" sets the same world of events into a pattern of personal relationships, specifically the covenant relationship between God and his people. Events, including those we would call physical, are here understood as occasions of meeting between personal beings, so that their meaning is to be found in willed action and the response it elicits, rather than as a series of physical-chemical changes. Thus, in the biblical world view, the full meaning of any event can be known only from within the personal encounter which it really is. The significance of the event lies in the personal confrontation, not in changes of place or physical state. In these terms, a whole picture of the natural order and the history of man is displayed as the life of dialogue with God.

Because of its personal basis, the content of biblical religion must be dealt with at two levels, rather than one only. The first and fundamental level is that of active participation. This is the act of faith, the declaration of himself, which the person makes as he responds in some fashion to the relationship offered by God in the covenant with Israel or in Christ. At this level adequate language requires action terms such as loyalty, commitment, passion, enthusiasm. This is the primordial level of being where we speak of religion as involving our passional natures, where the whole person, including also his rational nature, is engaged and committed. In this act of commitment, one establishes the structure of understanding, the goals and the pattern of relationship, within which he will interpret his experience. Here he lays the foundation of wholeness upon which experience rests, and sets the terms by which his life is organized and made meaningful.

The second level is the content of the biblical story of the career of Israel and the Christian community.

This is the world of events understood as the dialogue between God and man. The content of this picture of the world and of man's career has one striking similarity to our scientific world view, and at least two significant differences, aside from the relatively trivial, although conspicuous, cosmological difference.

The great similarity is that the biblical account is as insistently empirical as any scientific record. In spite of the common impression that the Bible is primarily a collection of moral commands, flavored with folklore and fortified by abstract speculations about the divine, in fact it is none of these. It is the record of the career of a people, first under an old covenant through Abraham and Moses, and then under a new one with the coming of Jesus the Christ. The claim of the Bible is that God was acting in the events of Israel's history, and biblical religion is actually concerned with both the record of these happenings and the continued participation in their significance. Such moral teaching or legislation as is given in the Bible stands within the record of the historical events as the way of making explicit the moral implications of the covenant relationship which was created by and fulfilled in these events. "Speculation" about the nature of the Christ, for example in the writings of St. Paul or in the Book of Hebrews, is not more speculative than the mathematical constructions of theoretical physicists. Both physicists and biblical writers attempt to make comprehensible the nature of the events men participate in. Both anchor their thought in the world of concrete empirical events.

The point that the Bible is empirical and not speculative may be emphasized by recalling the fact that nowhere in the Bible are there any discussions of the reality of God or attempts to demonstrate his actuality.

God's reality is simply taken for granted as the basis for Israel's existence. He is not made into a premise from which certain consequences are to be deduced. The biblical writers' assumption of God is like the scientist's realism: they do not question that a reality confronts them; the only question they are concerned with is what this reality is doing.

The biblical world view diverges from that of contemporary science first in the quality of its narrative. Where the scientist is expected to exclude his own desires or hopes or fears from his reports lest he permit these to affect his assessment of what is going on, the biblical account is no similar impassive, detached history of events whose outcome is indifferent to the narrator. Instead, it is a story. But the story is not a mere chronicle of the migrations of an ancient people in the Middle East, or of a group of believers gathered in the conviction that their crucified leader had been raised from the dead and was God himself. At its heart, it tells of God's actions in creating a world and a people for himself. It is the tragic but ultimately triumphant account of this people's reluctant and resistant response to God, of its failure to maintain the relationship he had called it to, and finally of the culmination of his efforts to restore and sustain relationship with man through his incarnation in Jesus Christ.

The Bible is salvation history, the recital of the saving acts of God, not a theoretical account of man's relation to God, or of God's ways with man, analyzing the terms of their relationship. Even the Book of Job, which many people assume to be a general analysis of the problem of suffering, ends by pointing harshly away from such generalities in Yahweh's challenge to Job. The Bible is not the story of man in general, but of specific men in specific times and places, among whom we also are numbered. Their personal story is also our own personal history. The content of biblical religion, therefore, is a personal story in the direct sense that in it and through it, the covenant is offered and received and man's broken participation redeemed.

Thus the great words of biblical religion must be set within the life of the covenant people who are gathered by God's action. They are not doctrines to be defined and defended, as if they were fixed things or characteristics like atomic weights. They are the qualities of relationship between man and God and between man and man within the community of faith. Such words in biblical religion as love, grace, sin, forgiveness, justice, mercy, and faithfulness all describe the way God deals with men, and the way men respond to God and to one another. When terms like these are applied to God or to man as if they were specific distinguishing traits like musical talent or bilateral symmetry, they are being grossly misused. Love is not a thing; it is a relationship. Forgiveness is not a nostrum applied like a salve; it is a relationship restored, not by forgetting what was done but by the determination that what was done will not be allowed to destroy the relationship. If one looks for forgiveness as he looks for a gain in weight, he will not find it—not because it is missing, but because it resides in the purposes and loyalties of the person, expressed in the way he participates with those around him. Grace is not a divine substance; it is God's attitude, the manner in which he deals with man, expressed in his forgiveness, and in his giving himself in Christ Jesus. In the same way, justice is not a rule of absolute equality used to measure rewards and punishments, but God's intention to restore to full and proper relationship those who have fallen away, and justice is not satisfied until the broken relationship has been restored. Sin is not a defect like sickle-cell anemia; it is rebellion against the relationship into which man has been called by God.

At the same time, such words as these represent the content of biblical religion, for they symbolize the understanding of experience, the appropriation and participation in the world of events, and therefore the knowledge of the world and of man and of God, that biblical religion espouses.

The second major distinction between the biblical and the scientific world views is that the biblical is eschatological. The course of events in the biblical story had a beginning with the creation and it moves to a final end, the eschaton, when the whole cosmic process will be fulfilled in the Kingdom of God. Biblical eschatology, by proclaiming this fulfillment at the end of time, sharply contrasts with our expectation that the processes of nature and history will continue indefinitely, and have no ultimate purpose or destination. The biblical story says that the whole cosmic process stands within the purposes of God who created it and who will bring it to fulfillment at the end of time in the Kingdom of God. Our popular insistence upon the desirability of progress, which got a powerful boost from evolutionary ideas, is a secularized form of biblical eschatology, but it lacks any sense of fulfillment at the end. The added conception of purpose, which is often smuggled into the notion of progress, fails to carry the full weight of the biblical idea, because the conception of a purpose working by evolutionary improvement lacks the essential biblical category of judgment. Moreover, both purpose and progress can be defined within a total configuration which itself has no ultimate purpose or destination, and is not subject to any judgment. Our conventional view says just this of human beings who do act in terms of their personal intentions but who are living within a total world which has neither purpose nor destination.

THE NEW HEAVEN AND THE NEW EARTH

IT is perhaps unfortunate that biblical eschatology should have been stated predominantly (although not solely) in apocalyptic terms, but no student of biblical religion can escape this flavor in the biblical story. What is given there consists of fantastic images which portray a cataclysmic termination of the present age, which is ruled by the powers of evil, in the war of Armageddon between these powers and God. The powers of evil will be destroyed, and God's victory will be followed by a thousand years of peace in which Christ will rule the world in righteousness. At the end of this millenium of peace, there will be the final judgment and the separation of righteous men who go to heaven from the evil ones who go to hell. With this final judgment the world will come to an end; the whole cosmic process which we now experience will cease to be.

This apocalyptic picture not only appears in the Old Testament; it runs through the New Testament, being spelled out in detail in the last book of the New Testament, Revelation, and it is put on the lips of Jesus in such narratives as Matthew 24–25 and Mark 13. Some Christian groups have identified the meaning of the Christian message and the content of biblical religion with the affirmation of this apocalyptic picture in its full and frightening detail. Others have rejected the apocalyptic picture, and in so doing have lost the intent of the eschatology.

Our contemporary view of the cosmic process has no place for such an end of the world. It is worth noting that neither an atomic holocaust which would make life impossible on the earth, nor the incineration of the earth if our sun becomes a supernova, satisfies the apocalyptic meaning. Either of these finales to the career of the earth, or at least to the career of man on the earth, would represent a normal, if unwelcome, course of events in the natural order as we already know it. These are "natural" events coherent with physical principles we are already acquainted with, whereas the apocalyptic end destroys nature as we know it and brings nature itself to an end.

Because we cannot accept the likelihood of such a divine destruction of the universe—even if we are willing to affirm God's creation of it—we are likely to miss the import of the eschatological view, which lies not in an apocalyptic drama of catastrophe, but in the reality of judgment and consummation. The apostolic community went forth proclaiming the end of the present age, and the dawn of the new messianic age in the Christ, whose life and mighty works inaugurated the new age which was to replace the old one. His resurrection certified for them that they had not been deceived in their faith in him. They were a colony of heaven, living in the interim between the two worlds, a foretaste of the new age while still participating in the old world which was condemned to destruction. The stupendous events associated with Christ, in which they participated, specifically his resurrection, marked the incursion of this new age into the old. The Kingdom of God was in truth come, and they were members of its new life in the midst of the old. It was true that the Kingdom had not fully come, but there could no longer be any doubt about its actuality, for they themselves shared its life, and lived by its power in their midst.

The apostles and the church were not talking about some interior experience confined to a change of idea or attitude or emotion, but about the concrete life of men with each other, personally, socially, and economically. It was this life which had been found wanting and which was to be replaced by the new world. They believed that the consummation of the promised Kingdom would come in its complete form soon and violently, and many of the apostolic community apparently expected to live to see its coming, but the form of the fulfillment was less significant for their thought than its actuality. However, as the hope of an imminent end faded with the delay of the apocalyptic war of Armageddon, the nature of the Kingdom of God tended, more and more, either to be interiorized as some kind of attitude, or to be translated into terms of a life after death located in heaven as a place or state which one enters upon when he dies. This process of interiorizing or spiritualizing the culmination has blunted the thrust of the eschatological view as it appears in the biblical record.

However the end is supposed to come, biblical eschatology both declares the power of the Kingdom of God in this world as it now exists, and condemns this world for failing to attain the quality of life God conceives for his covenanted people. Therefore, life as now lived is condemned and must be replaced by another life which is the Kingdom of God. Eschatology as judgment means that the life of man, individual and social, must come to terms with God's actions and intentions.

Biblically speaking, because life and the cosmic

process move to a destination, and are there judged, the whole career of man is to be understood in terms of God's purposes in creating and redeeming the world. Man's career, therefore, has meaning as he responds to God's purposeful and meaningful activity. When he responds as a believer, he becomes a participant in God's design for the whole world. It is God's intention that men shall live together in his Kingdom, under his rule, and the fact that they do not now so live means that the present quality of life must be replaced by another world. And the only vivid language in which to say this is by talking about the end of this world.

Eschatology also declares the conquest of evil, whether or not one affirms the apocalyptic form of the victory. Despite our experience that the powers of evil appear to be in control, they are not victorious at all. They have already been defeated; the resurrection is the great sign of their defeat, and the believing community shares in that victory, soon to be made apparent in its full form. Eschatology is the biblical way of announcing God's ultimate victory by reading the signs already given of that victory.

The possibility now offered to men is that they accept the victory and participate in its fulfillment by joining the community of those who are in the Kingdom. For those who accept the invitation, the life of the Kingdom of God then becomes the standard by which they live during the interval before the old world passes away. What the New Testament has to say about ethics is simply a description of the character of the new life of the Kingdom. The fact that the world is not yet the Kingdom, indeed that it refuses to be of the Kingdom, means that persecution and suffering will be the lot of those who accept the call to share now in the new life.

Their suffering does not, however, signify failure; it is the way the quality of the Kingdom is exhibited to an unbelieving world, and it is the way that world is brought to repentance and victorious response.

The early Christian community had a keen sense that God's spirit was in their midst, leading them directly in their life and activities. This awareness was another sign of the authenticity of the Kingdom and of their participation in it. The risen Christ was with them, guiding and supporting and comforting them. They could face with unquenchable courage the most terrible threats and tortures because they knew they shared the coming victory of God, and their sufferings confirmed their participation in his Kingdom. In the light of this assurance about their relation to God, they developed a new set of values by which to measure the significance of the events of their daily life. They could be courageous and heedless because they were really strangers in this world; they belonged to the new world whose coming they already shared in.

THE LIFE OF DIALOGUE

THE biblical story, which looks back to the creation of the world and forward to the end of time, is focussed upon the history of a people in covenant with God, a people whose life is continued in the community of Christian believers today. Within this story, the meaning of the covenant relationship found several forms as Israel and her leaders variously understood the obligations and privileges of their relationship to God. The question of how Israel should respond was the source of the prophets' continuing attack on their people's tendency to rest easy in a secure contract with God. The biblical story makes it plain that Israel never enjoyed this kind of security but instead that the covenant meant dialogue with God.

It is essential to dialogue that each participant shall respond to the action of the other in a relationship of responsible exchange. Between human beings, dialogue is properly an exchange between equals who grant to each other full freedom to be themselves, and who welcome from each other the fullest and freest, the most responsible, expression of the self. Between unequals, as between God and man, dialogue consists in the superior permitting the other to be a person in his own right, as one who contributes and declares himself, rather than as an object coerced into a predetermined reaction.

In the biblical picture, while men are equal to each other in the sense that they all are created beings, man is never the equal of God. Both the priority and the initiative in all aspects of their relationship belong to God. Hence God cannot be captured in a cage of neutral categories of law, or universal principles or fixed relationships which guarantee God to man and permit man to manipulate God. The sin of idolatry in the Bible was not the sin of sexuality in religion—although the Hebrews rejected that—but the sin of making God into an auxiliary to a contract, so that he had to obey the rules and respond with fruitful flocks and fields when men performed their part of the ritual cycle. The God of the Bible is not thus subject to man's will or desires, and woe to any man who lightly enters into covenant with the biblical God, and who then attempts to reduce God to a principle or a force which can be used and controlled, as men controlled the nature deities of the fertility cults.

If, like Israel, one accepts God's invitation and

enters into covenant with God, and then fails to respond as he engaged himself to do, he discovers that God is the relentless lover, the Hound of Heaven, who will not abandon him to his desired oblivion. Because God loves, he will seek man out and if necessary punish him, as Israel was sent into Exile, until he returns to the full life of the covenant.

The biblical pattern of meaning extends personal meeting with God to include the natural order which God created to be the theater of man's own history. The Bible has no awareness of a self-sustaining, impersonal, natural order running according to its own intrinsic laws. Certainly the natural world is as dependable and regular as science has found it to be, but these regularities are manifestations of God's faithfulness and trustworthiness. As Jesus said, the rain falls on the just and the unjust alike, not because precipitation results from mechanical collisions of air masses and shifting temperatures, and is indifferent to persons, but because God who makes the rain fall is directly concerned for the welfare of all his creatures, including those who reject him. The universality of God's concern does not mean that he is morally indifferent. It means that he is infinitely dependable and faithful, even when man is neither. When the Old Testament writers ascribed rain and harvest, or drought and famine, to God, they were not providing an anthropomorphic meteorology which we can today abandon. They were insisting that their dependence upon the course of nature was one form of dependence upon God, because he was the source of nature. They were in fact remarking on how fortunate they were that God watered their land by rains, instead of their having to make their own arrangements through irrigation. Order is rooted in God, not things, in the biblical view. Nature is not the clue to God, but God is the clue to nature.

When the biblical pattern of meaning is translated into moral terms, the situation is the same as with nature. The world of the Bible has a moral structure which every man discerns in his own moral sensibilities, and he trifles with this structure to his doom. But this structure of goodness and righteousness is not an impassible and immutable frame imposed upon man and to which he must submit or shatter himself upon in futile resistance, and the end is not an impersonal destiny fixed by the fates but willed destination. The nature of goodness and righteousness are demonstrated by God in his actions; their depths are disclosed in God's redemptive activity; and man's goodness lies in his willing responsiveness to God. God acts to save, not merely to create and test. He is not satisfied with punishing those who fail and rewarding those who succeed in obeying his will. Thus the height of man's responsiveness is measured not by his obedience but by his repentance, in which he wills to return to the relationship he has broken, and it is in repentance and restoration that the Bible discovers the full moral order of the universe.

The pattern of man's response can be described in a code, but it cannot be confined to the code without reducing God to a static thing and the covenant relationship to a mere payment of earned rewards. Those who read the Bible as a compendium of God's moral demands, and accordingly see biblical religion as a matter of fulfilling certain requirements, deny the life of dialogue. They turn God into an idol, albeit a moral one, before which we can walk securely because the code gauges our pace as clearly as do the charts that diagram dance steps. However useful such charts may be in training faltering feet, he who can only move by the chart may keep time with the music, but he does not dance.

Man's actual participation in the covenant dialogue has been more rebellious than receptive. In biblical language, this is sin. We have persistently responded unwillingly and resentfully, egotistically desiring to dominate the situation, and twisting the web of exchange in order to use, for our own purposes, the others with whom we are involved. What should have been a relationship of mutual support has become predatory instead, so that, as St. Paul says, the whole creation groans and travails until now.[1] In our relationship with God, we have behaved no better. Instead of rejoicing at being a servant in the fulfillment of God's purposes, we —like Israel—have sought only the promised reward, and looked upon whatever peace, prosperity, and power we have as being indubitable proof of superior virtue.

Man's sinful rebellion provides the groundwork for the biblical estimate of man. Yet sin is neither an *a priori* axiom, nor a simple—but dreadful—interpretative category. It is the condition of resistance and resentment we discover in ourselves through our relationship with God and our fellows. And we discover this quality in ourselves because response carries responsibility. If one simply reacts to an external push, then that external force carries whatever responsibility there is. But in biblical religion, man himself is responsible for his decisions, because the biblical question demands response and not a reaction. The wandering Israelites in the wilderness rebelled against Moses because they were afraid of their unknown future and longed for the security of their known past. They reacted with fear to

[1] Romans 8:22.

the strains of nomadic life, and responded to fear with a plea to be relieved of responsibility. It would have been better, they said, to have remained well-fed slaves in Egypt. But they could not unload the responsibility for their situation on Moses or upon the conditions around them, and neither can we. We may not have set the circumstances within which we live, but we are responsible for the way we act within them. On a deeper level, Isaiah's vision of God was not nearly so much a penetration of the veil which hides God, as it was a tearing away of the barrier which concealed Isaiah from himself, so that he could not, as his ancestors did, blame someone else for his condition. In God's presence he saw himself, "Woe is me! for I am lost; . . . for my eyes have seen the King, the Lord of Hosts."[2] The biblical account is not an attempt to prove the conclusion that man is a sinner; it exhibits the consequences of sin in the history of man.

Further, the Bible does not present man's sinfulness as simply a warping of the will so that his will is at odds with his rational capacity. It declares instead that what constitutes reason and rationality is the whole person in response. Reason is not a fraction of man's nature or a single element which rules—or should rule—the remainder of his being. Reasoning is one of the ways in which the whole person responds; it is one form of personal action by which the whole person strives for a coherent existence. There is no promise in the biblical story that if this coherence could be achieved in abstract rational terms according to the pattern of a neutral and universal truth, as in the Cartesian view of pure reason, and our contemporary computer model of pure rational-

[2] Isaiah 6:5.

ity, then we would possess pure truth and be perfect, sinless beings. The biblical story neither suggests that the Israelites intended to do the right but lacked proper information, nor that they possessed the clear truth in rational terms but willfully rejected the clear leading of their minds. Instead, the Bible records the whole person acting: what one finds to be reasonable and the way he reasons expresses his whole being. It expresses the commitments he has made and his struggles to be obedient to what he has promised. If that person, as the biblical insight shows, is sinful, then his reason itself shares his sin.

REVELATION IN DIALOGUE

IF the biblical view is to be taken seriously, God's action cannot be described in neutral, impersonal terms as a kind of spiritual gravitational attraction, acting uniformly in all directions as a constant factor to be entered in our moral calculations, as gravitational attraction is entered in the computation of orbits of planets or artificial satellites. The God of the Bible is not the eternal bystander before whose face the generations rise and pass away. He is the chief actor in the career of man, and the central question in every event is what disclosure of himself and his will he gives in that event in our history.

When we speak of God as the God of history, we are not simply providing a theistic causal explanation of how events go, as a corrective to the notion that causes should be sought in social, economic, geographical, political, or psychological factors. Instead, the biblical story says that the question man always faces is what is God doing with us and for us in this concrete social, economic situation in our individual and national life, for he uses our history as his way of seeking us out to restore us to our proper relationship with himself.

Biblical religion does not predicate that if we explore our experience more minutely, we will discover a divine factor operating among the earthly factors already identified. Still less does it contain the notion that we postulate that divine factor to explain ourselves. In contrast to both of these interpretations, biblical religion proclaims that God has initiated our existence in dialogue with himself, as his way of revealing himself to us.

Because this is a dialogue of personal beings, however, it follows that God is hidden behind his actions. He is not transparent to our analysis; his inner nature is no more accessible than is that of one human being to another, despite the impression some novelists give when they display the inner consciousness of their characters. The hiddenness of God is not due simply to the distance between his infinity and our finiteness. The *deus absconditus* is not merely a medieval theological phrase expressing his remoteness. God's actuality is necessarily hidden behind his action because every personal being is a mystery, an enigma wearing a mask of acts, and no being can open himself fully to another, even when he tries.

The essence of personal nature is to be a center of willing, purposing action, a nucleus of integrity and wholeness. Fully to open one's own center of being to another—if it were possible at all—would substitute the other for oneself and thereby obliterate oneself. Fully to occupy another's center of being is to obliterate him. So it is also in the biblical view of man's relationship with God. God acts to reveal himself, but because his action occurs necessarily within the dialogue between personal beings in the concrete events of history, the authenticity of man's being is never denied. The Bible offers no revelatory process which, by standing outside the meeting of personal beings in real events, would be exempt from the limitations and ambiguities of man's actual existence. For this reason the biblical revelation is the recounting of the career of an actual people, Israel, and its continuation in the New Testament community of faith, and because man both participates in the recorded events and interprets their meaning, the Bible contains neither an unambiguous self-disclosure by God, nor a set of final propositions about his nature and will. Since man participates in the meeting, its final product of action or word must contain some element and effect of the receptive person as well as of the initiating person. Not everyone who reads the New Testament will find in Jesus the God who reconciles the world unto himself, just as it is indubitable that many people who heard him in the flesh failed to recognize God in him.

This biblical view of revelation as a meeting of persons must be distinguished from two other current concepts. One equates revelation with discovery. In discovery, however, the initiative belongs to the inquirer himself, while in revelation the initiative belongs to God. Still less can revelation be equated with the discovery of stupendous or disconcerting news, despite the popular misuse of the word in this way. If revelation is discovery, whatever man knows he has dug out for himself, as when we "think God's thoughts after him" by unravelling the mathematics of celestial mechanics, for in this situation God or nature volunteers no answers. To the contrary, biblical religion is concerned with God's actions and man's responses, not simply with man's explorations or speculations.

The other view preserves the initiative of God, but denies the dialogue with man. Here, revelation is identified with formal statements of the truth, framed and delivered by God himself. With depressing frequency, both nonbelievers and sincere believers declare the Bible to be such a collection of divine propositions. The emphasis in this view is upon content, not contact. In these terms, Christianity, as a revealed religion, is a deposit of teachings, organization, practices, rituals, and perhaps its history, which were delivered intact by God to man. Strictly speaking, Christianity so understood could have no history, only a duration, for divine perfection can exhibit no change and there is no possibility of dialogue with such a truth.

This propositional view of revelation is extremely tempting because it offers the security of certain and inviolable truth. There could be no doubt about the content of such a religion. Nevertheless, no such security appears in the biblical story. God failed to guard his disclosure of himself in Jesus Christ with any such unmistakable assurance. Instead, even with the Christ he required men to make a decision about himself, and Christians believe that many men have made the wrong decision, both then and now.

Revelation as a secure and certain content denies the integrity of the person to whom it is delivered. One can have no dialogue with such a truth, because one has no freedom at all in the presence of a final and complete truth, and indeed, what we mean by proof or demonstration is that we are not free to reject it. When God's authenticity becomes a matter of proof, no one is free any longer to refuse him. When revelation is propositional, the source controls the content so that its accuracy is guaranteed. There can be no meeting of persons, for by his interaction man would only add noise to the circuits and confuse the message. A content definition of revelation eliminates all ambiguity in our recognition of the truth, and by so doing it denies the biblical view that we are responsible persons in relationshp with God.

Revelation as the encounter in which God meets man means that God reveals himself, not propositions about himself. Without such self-disclosure of God, we would know nothing of his nature and perhaps nothing of his being. But what we do know is God himself, not facts about him, and what Christians claim to know of God is Christ, not certain statements about this figure which are recorded in the Bible and proclaimed in the Christian creeds.

The biblical story stands within the encounter between God and man as a description and symbol, as an interpretation and celebration, of that meeting. The community of faith, the Israel of God described in the Bible and continued in the Christian church, is both the consequence of that revelatory confrontation of man by God, and the continuing occasion of confrontation. Because the community of faith lives in its specific time and place, its structure and judgments cannot be a formal and final statement of the content of God's self-disclosure any more than the words of the Bible itself can be. Through the Bible and the community of believers, God is communicated and the encounter renewed, although neither Bible nor community provides us with specific formulas which are to be defended as the literal and ultimate truth about God or his activity.

The words of biblical religion, therefore, bear two

stamps. One comes from the God who initiated the meeting and sustains the relationship of exchange in which man lives, and our words—the biblical words—refer to him as the source of all existence. They do not refer to some creature of our own thoughts. The other stamp on these words comes from ourselves and our forerunners in the faith, as those who are met, who respond, and who speak out of the whole texture of understanding and experience which mark our own or their specific and unique location in the history of man.

The revelatory process as defined in biblical religion shows man as a specific self living in a certain time and place, being met by God, and being called to respond to God within the concrete conditions of his historical situation. There is no such thing in biblical religion as man in general without bonds to time and society. Man always speaks out of his own time and place, and his words necessarily reflect that situation.

It would be easy to conclude, therefore, that the biblical words and biblical religion present nothing but a specific primitive cultural situation long since gone. This is the conclusion of those who find the Bible simply to be a record of the parochial ideas of the Hebrews and of the primitive Christian community. And many people find no more than this in the Old Testament when they read the grim stories of a vengeful tribal deity who prompted the Hebrews to total war against the Canaanites, whose only crime was that they were on the ground first.

But the biblical record is not *the* revelation. It is the *occasion* for revelation, and those who wrote it spoke from their own revelatory meeting in order that they might continue that meeting, and nourish and extend the community of the people of God created by the revelatory meeting. They understood themselves as concrete beings, with wills, purposes, desires and demands, who were confronted by an equally concrete but divine being whose purposes and will created and sustained their own existence as persons and as a people. Their career depended upon how they responded and participated in the relationship of covenant into which God had invited them. Their story culminated in God's redemptive activity in Christ when he acted to restore the relationship which man's rebellion had all but destroyed. That redemptive activity was not restricted to the specific cultural group within which he appeared, but included all men and extended throughout all the future to its consummation at the end of time, just as it reached into the past to the moment of creation itself. According to the biblical view, we also are standing within that relationship as specific beings in our own time and culture, invited by the biblical story to become participants in the community of faith, to accept our relationship of exchange with God, and thus to participate in the revelatory dialogue out of which biblical religion came.

To state this biblical claim does not, however, constitute proof of its truth. To assert that we will understand ourselves and make our experience coherent only if we organize that experience in terms of this biblical world view, does not demonstrate the truth of that understanding. It is one thing to describe a point of view or way of interpreting oneself and the world. It is another thing to determine whether that understanding is true, and whether it constitutes knowledge.

The pivot upon which this question turns is the nature of proof. By what we will accept as proof, we define what we mean by truth and set the boundaries of knowledge.

✸ *Chapter Four*

THE BASIS OF AUTHORITY

For the word of the cross is folly to those who are perishing, but to us who are being saved it is the power of God. For it is written, "I will destroy the wisdom of the wise, and the cleverness of the clever I will thwart." Where is the wise man? Where is the scribe? Where is the debater of this age? Has not God made foolish the wisdom of the world? For since, in the wisdom of God, the world did not know God through wisdom, it pleased God through the folly of what we preach to save those who believe. For Jews demand signs and Greeks seek wisdom, but we preach Christ crucified, a stumbling-block to Jews and folly to Gentiles, but to those who are called, both Jews and Greeks, Christ the power of God and the wisdom of God. For the foolishness of God is wiser than men, and the weakness of God is stronger than men. I CORINTHIANS 1:18–25

THE PROBLEM OF PROOF

WHEN the Christian believer is asked whether Christianity is true, and whether it is the religion for all men, he will answer "Yes." His difficulties begin when he is asked to prove this claim. He may appeal to the Bible, or to the teachings of the Christian churches, or to the creeds, or perhaps to the self-evident persuasiveness of his assertion. None of these supports for his claim demonstrate its truth, for all stand within the tradition which is to be validated. This kind of proof is circular, and it is just that circle that our scientific predilections prompt us to break.

The problem of proof in religion is the problem of what is to count as evidence, for what the believer proposes as evidence will not necessarily be acceptable to those who are outside the believing community. It would be far more satisfactory to point to some specific event which all men could see, whether they are believers or not, and to rest the case upon data about events which all people can observe. It would be much more persuasive to be able to perform experiments with the phenomena of religious experience as scientists can experiment with their phenomena, to make predictions about future events as the scientists do, and to have the same kind of certainty the sciences apparently have.[1]

The effort to give religion the same kind and degree of certainty that science has raises two difficulties. One is that while there is a body of data in religion which we can validate in a scientific fashion, we are actually then dealing with scientific questions, not religious ones. It is legitimate to ask what happened when, for example, Moses saw the burning bush or spoke with Yahweh on Mt. Sinai, or where and how the Israelites crossed the Sea of Reeds, and how Jericho was conquered. Within limits, depending on the data available, we can say something about what did happen. In asking this question and answering it in this fashion,

[1] Cf. Franklin Loehr, *The Power of Prayer on Plants* (Garden City, N.Y.: Doubleday and Co., 1959). A glaring example of the assumption that scientific categories are sovereign in all areas.

however, the essential religious question and its answer escape around the corners of the scientific data. The other difficulty points in the same direction. We can attain the apparent precision and security of a scientific demonstration only by doing what scientific methodology does, namely, removing the responding, participating person from the situation. We can have this kind of certainty in dealing with religious phenomena and in answering questions about religious claims only at the cost of denying or excluding the personal response which makes religion authentic in the first place.

The historical character of biblical religion means that the events in the biblical story are also part of the secular history of the Levant. The settlement of the Hebrews in what they called the Promised Land is part of the Semitic migrations through the Fertile Crescent. The rise and decline of the Davidic empire is a footnote to the struggle between Egypt and Mesopotamia for dominance over each other, and for control of the Palestinian battleground lying between them. The captivity of the southern kingdom, Judah, in Babylonia belongs to the rise and the fall of that empire before the growing pressure of Persia under Cyrus. Rome provided the context for Jesus and the apostles. One of her governors presided at the condemnation of Jesus to the cross, and the *pax Romana* made Paul's travels possible. The history of Christianity in Europe cannot be separated from the political, economic, and cultural history of Europe, and the spread of Christianity around the world is part of the story of the rise of western civilization to its current position of cultural dominance.

All these events and a multitude more, as well as the details of the inner growth of the tradition, belong to the province of secular history so far as questions of method, accuracy, and authenticity are concerned. The problems of recovering an authentic text are the same for Moses or Plato or St. Paul. While the discoveries of the Dead Sea Scrolls have excited the world of biblical studies, their collection and interpretation are a matter of scholarship in the same sense as scholarship is pursued in any other field of historical and literary research. When this kind of scientific investigation shows that data reported in the biblical narrative or in Christian history are mistaken in time, or person named, or city captured, we revise the record of these details accordingly. No aspect of the historical record of biblical religion within the Bible or since is exempt from this kind of test. By its means the authorship and literary history of the biblical writings has been determined, and such documents as the "Donation of Constantine" shown to be fraudulent. Long and intricate books have been written to report the history of the Hebrews and the Christian movement, both to correct and to fill in the gaps of the biblical record and to complete the story since biblical times. This is a scientific enterprise, and it answers scientific questions about biblical religion, not the religious question.

Our scientific predispositions have led us to assume that if the events of the biblical story could be established on neutral, impartial grounds which the unbeliever would also accept, then biblical religion would be secure, and belief in the truth of biblical religion would be fully justified. However, achieving this historical verification does not demonstrate the truth of biblical religion. It only documents its ineradicable historical roots. While scientific study of biblical religion is possible and desirable, it can establish only what scientific study can achieve; such study does not touch the center of the biblical claim.

The historical character of biblical religion does not imply that it will be possible to provide an impartial account of events or a definitive body of facts by which to prove to the unbeliever that he is making a mistake. And any religion, biblical or other, which defines itself in such terms will paralyze the personal responsiveness and participation which are central to dialogue. Those who speak from within the covenant relationship, speak *from* their experience, to invite others to share their experience, not in order to prove the correctness of their experience. Therefore, no conclusive demonstration of the authenticity of the covenant is possible outside that covenant relationship.

The biblical question, "Who are you in response to God, the creator and redeemer revealed in Jesus Christ?" cannot be answered with pieces of evidence from the natural and historical record. But neither can it be answered in the absence of evidence from the historical record, because the dialogue between God and man, which biblical religion is, necessarily takes place within history. This is the dilemma infecting all truth claims in biblical religion: that there is both a person who must declare himself, and an external world with a character of its own. In biblical terms, God confronts us in his actions (which are also the events of the natural and social world around us) with the demand that we respond in relationship to him, not merely react to the forces of the external world. The question that biblical religion poses does not ask us simply to describe correctly God's actions in that external world, nor does it provide any escape from the character and pressures of that world. Instead it demands a response, that is, a choice between meanings by which to live in the actual world where we are, and the character of our response determines what we can know about that world and how we will validate our understanding of it.

In biblical terms, therefore, validation consists not of correctly describing a succession of occurrences, but of measuring experience against the meaning one has chosen in the consciousness that one must live with and act upon the consequences of that choice. The biblical picture of man and his career is finally true if, by participating in its style of relationship, the person finds that his actions fit coherently into the totality of events. That is, the picture is validated if it confirms and authenticates for him his participation as a person in the world. This has always been the claim of biblical religion: that, in its terms, man will know who he is.

There is no corollary promise that such a recognition of oneself will be either comfortable or welcome; there is the promise that it will make one's existence authentic, even though in it one recognizes himself as a sinner, for the biblical picture of man's career proclaims the redemption of sinners and the healing of broken relationships. One who has received forgiveness and experienced its healing knows that it is true. He knows that the only understanding of the world possible for him blazons and sustains this transformation. But he who has not received forgiveness because he has not known himself as a repentant sinner is not qualified to judge the validity of this demonstration. Just as one who knows nothing more of mathematics than simple arithmetic will not deserve or get a hearing from physicists, so one whose attitudes toward biblical religion are dominated by childhood prejudices, and whose information is confined to a few Sunday school stories of the patriarchs or secondhand hearsay accounts of what goes on in churches, does not deserve and should not receive a hearing on matters of biblical religion. Competence is demanded in religious matters as much as in scientific ones and competence consists in personal experience of the relationships—scientific or religious—which are being proclaimed and celebrated.

If this seems to be an unsatisfactory basis for demonstration in religion, it is likely to be because religion most clearly reveals the dilemma of our existence. We must act, but we cannot know with complete certainty whether we have chosen the right form of action. We must choose, but we cannot demonstrate with logical certitude the correctness of our choice when we confront someone who has chosen another model as the clue to his existence.

THE PERSON IN THE EVENT

THE resurrection of Jesus from the dead exhibits more clearly than any other event the dilemma that response and participation are constituent parts of the events of the biblical tradition. Many other claims about him—his miraculous powers, his virgin birth, his singular authority—are difficult enough, although historical research may reduce some of their embarrassment for us. For example, most people today assume that the virgin birth attests the deity of Jesus: he is proved to be God by the miraculous character of his birth. On the contrary, investigation of the literature of the early period of Christian thought shows clearly that the original intention of the claim was to prove his humanity. The emphasis was not upon a miraculous conception but upon the actuality of his birth from Mary, for anyone born of a human mother must be authentically human.

The issue arose from the question whether the Christ, whose deity was universally affirmed, was also authentically human or whether (as the Docetists claimed) his human form was an appearance, a veil, a disguise. When the doctrine of the virgin birth of Jesus is seen in this light, it immediately becomes apparent that modern discussion of the biological possibility of parthenogenesis in human beings does not even meet the question, much less answer it. For the resurrection, however, we do not have even this slight—if ultimately irrelevant—biological prop.

The resurrection of Jesus is the central event in the Christian proclamation. Without it, nothing else in the biblical story is very important for Christianity. At the same time, no other purported event in the biblical record is more awkward for historians to treat with their tools of investigation and canons of scientific truth. If this event was what the disciples apparently believed it to be, then by its nature it cannot be naturalized and accommodated to the usual canons of scientific demonstration if only because there is no other similar event in history with which it can be compared.[2] Although it is a commonplace that historical events are singular and unrepeatable—so also are scientific events, if less obviously such—nevertheless, there are types and resemblances among historical events which make it possible to compare battles or kings or economic systems and political decisions. The Easter event is the ultimate example of an event which has no peers. No myth of a dying and rising god will serve, precisely because such narratives are, in the popular

[2] Cf. Richard R. Niebuhr, *Resurrection and Historical Reason: A Study of Theological Method* (New York: Charles Scribner's Sons, 1957). A careful examination of the problem involved in historical validation of the resurrection.

sense of the term, myths; no claim is made that they ever happened as historical events. The resurrection of Jesus Christ did occur in history, or, at least, so Christians declare.

The records make it ineluctably clear that the disciples were persuaded that something real had happened, but what happened cannot be described in the terms we use to identify or account for other events, without dissolving the disciples' claims. The only description that seems to fit the resurrection of Jesus into our ordinary world denies *a priori* their evidence by turning it into an internal kind of psychic disturbance which some of the disciples experienced while still tortured by grief and frustrated hopes.

Whether the disciples were correct or not, it is indubitable that they believed Jesus had been raised from the dead. They believed, and asserted that they were witnesses to the fact that the one whom they had seen die on the cross was alive again and as authentically in their midst as he had been before the crucifixion. In the light of this event, they were new men; the whole meaning and therefore the structure of their existence had changed. Now they had hope and confidence where before they had been without hope. Even time and the fate of the world had a new pattern. Now they participated in the victory of God over the powers of darkness and death which had ruled their lives until then. Because of the resurrection of Jesus, a new world had been born to replace the old world condemned to destruction, and in the resurrection, God had proclaimed him to be the Christ through whom all who so desired could enter this new life.

The question is: What kind of event are we dealing with? Is it the physiological assertion that a dead body had been reanimated, and in its reanimated state possessed odd qualities, such as the capacity to appear and disappear at will, and also to take food and present every indication of materiality?[3] Or is the event contained in the assertion that God had acted uniquely and triumphantly in Jesus to give new life to men and the world? Or is it an example of what can happen when an enthusiastically held belief gets going, so that the new life the disciples claimed was generated by their belief in the resurrection? These are not identical questions, and they are not answered in identical terms; yet neither are they wholly separable from each other.

That the disciples did have a new spirit after the resurrection event seems clear enough. The question has to do with the basis of that new life. The claim that God acted uniquely in this event to redeem mankind cannot be demonstrated in the same neutral fashion by which, presumably, the physiological aspects of the resurrection might conceivably be established. Our present physical bodies possess physiological factors, such as blood chemistry, which proceed independently of any intentions or attitudes on the part of an external observer. Presumably similar physiological indications of a resurrected body could be exhibited in independent and neutral terms.

For biblical religion, however, the physiological phenomenon in itself is of no great significance. It may be more startling to us than it was to the people of the first century, but it is of no great importance to learn that some, at least, of the physiological processes associated with death can be reversed and the body restored to the living state. It may be upsetting to learn that a

[3] Cf. Luke 24:13–50, the appearance to the two disciples on the way to Emmaus; John 20:24–29, the appearance to Thomas.

being in this restored state has properties unlike those we normally associate with life, such as the ability to pass through closed doors and to appear and disappear at will. If this is true, the world of nature is larger than we thought it was, but it is still intrinsically the same world, and we can continue to deal with it in much the same manner as before. This larger world would have possibilities we did not expect, but by extrapolating from our present knowledge we could anticipate the direction the pattern would go. God could be said to be related to the world and ourselves in a way analogous to the way a being from a four-dimensional world would be related to beings confined to a three-dimensional world. Our difficulties in perceiving Jesus' nature would be analogous to those which a two-dimensional being would have in dealing with a three-dimensional creature, and the resurrection of Jesus would become simply a visual demonstration of the "odd" character of this larger, but still entirely natural world.[4] There is reason for believing that such attempts to "naturalize" the resurrection began very early. It is probable that such details as the story of the empty tomb were prompted by the attempt to make the resurrection event a publicly demonstrable, physical one, independent of the believer's own commitment.

It is interesting to note that the New Testament records no observations of the resurrection itself. All accounts refer to appearances of the risen Christ. None are reports from persons who saw him being raised up

[4] Cf. Karl Heim, *Christian Faith and Natural Science* (New York: Harper and Row, 1953), pp. 159 ff. God is here interpreted as an additional space beyond our normal three dimensional space-time world. Cf. E. A. Abbott, *Flatland: A Romance of Many Dimensions,* 6th edition revised (Oxford: Basil Blackwell, 1950), a classic and entertaining exposition of the plurality of dimensions.

as Lazarus is reported to have been seen being raised from the dead.[5] Neither is there any biblical evidence that the event occurred on the first day of the week, as our Easter hymns declare. Rather it was on the first day of the week that the disciples became aware that this momentous event had occurred. Moreover, it is not possible to squeeze three days, in any ordinary understanding of this time span, into the interval between burial on Sabbath eve (Friday afternoon) and dawn of the first day of the week (Sunday).

Two further comments on the physiological aspects of the resurrection event are required. One is that from this distance, the details are too scanty to provide any working basis for the sort of research and verification that scientific historiography requires. The only thing we can say with assurance in terms of scientific historiography is that the disciples firmly believed that the resurrection had occurred, and that they proclaimed that fact as the center of their message. The echoes of the event come to us through words preserved by the community of faith which their preaching created, not through any independent remains or records.

The other comment is that our own knowledge of the natural world is neither so complete nor definitive that we can with confidence say exactly what is possible and what is impossible. Resurrections are not to be expected, because so far as our knowledge goes, the physiological processes associated with death are irreversible.[6] Yet the Christian proclamation embodied in the creeds is that there will be a general resurrection,

[5] John 11:43–44.

[6] It is worth noting that present-day stories of "medical miracles," in which "dead" people are restored to life, invariably play upon the ambiguity in what is meant by death.

and that the resurrection of Jesus Christ was the anticipation of this event, "the first fruits of those who have fallen asleep."[7] Our knowledge of the natural world does not put us in a position to be dogmatic about the impossibility of this event. Neither do we have the kind of data that would enable us confidently to defend it in the same neutral and disinterested terms we might be willing to defend the physiological actuality of the crucifixion of Jesus, or the assassination of Julius Caesar.

More is at stake in the resurrection story than a physiological event which anyone can note whether it is important to him or not. It is too late to revise the hymns we sing on Easter, but it is not too late to recognize the kind of event the resurrection is asserted by the Bible to be. It was not solely or primarily a physiological kind of thing, nor can it be said to be a purely internal and "psychic" event transpiring wholly within the thoughts and emotions of a few bereaved friends of Jesus.

To see the resurrected Christ, to apprehend the Easter event, required personal participation and response from the disciples. It was possible for them to see the resurrected Christ because they were already believers, not in the resurrection as such, for they were apparently not prepared for that, but in Jesus' power to give their lives and the whole world a new meaning. This does not mean that their "seeing" him was simply a product of their belief. The Easter event was more than merely a physical transaction which they were fortunate enough to observe. The event in full reality included their response as an essential part. The situation in the Easter event is parallel to the situation of

[7] I Corinthians 15:20.

Jesus before his crucifixion. Many people saw him and heard his words: only a few recognized him as the Messiah.

There are two parts to an event: an external happening, which may be described as some physical change of state or place, and the response contributed by the participants to make it the total thing it is. The resurrection of Jesus was both an event in the external world which captured and supported the disciples' believing response, and a personal response of commitment. We cannot, therefore, speak of the resurrection event without including both halves of the transaction. It was an event in whose light they could see a decisive change in the whole meaning of human existence. They had been shifted to a new center of integration where they could now see the new world as their own possession. They found themselves new persons, living a new existence because they shared in God's victory over death.

In other words, the resurrection, like all events, *is* really its full meaning. Some events perhaps can be satisfactorily comprised in the terms of a solely physical-chemical meaning. Others cannot be so confined in their meaning, because they are events in which one discovers who he is, in which he declares who he is by accepting himself as one whose existence is at stake in the event. The resurrection is supremely an event whose meaning cannot be confined to physical-chemical terms, for it offers and demands that one accept himself and respond as one for whom Christ died. Therefore, the resurrection as an event is available only to those who affirm this full meaning as the basis of their own lives. One who rejects this meaning has disqualified himself to experience the resurrection.

The issue has now become not the event itself, but

that of the meaning which is adequate to cope with the event, because any account of the event sets it within some form of relationship and context of meaning. One who confines his participation, and therefore the meaning of events, to the disinterested observation of physical changes, does not make himself available to this larger meaning demanded by the resurrection of Jesus Christ. His commitment to a certain narrow kind of meaning forecloses the possibility of appropriating other meanings. All that he can discover in his detached and physical terms is whether another person does or does not believe in the given notion. Whether the notion is true or false cannot be decided on neutral grounds which presuppose no commitment at all. The truth can be assessed only on the basis of some commitment of the self in which the choice between alternative meanings becomes a crucial matter for the one who judges. Only when the choice makes a difference to him in the way he responds to the world around him and in the meaning he finds in experience, can he really decide whether the claim is true or false. And then the meaning he has chosen identifies the truth that he will find.

We have long tried to conceal the thrust of this problem from ourselves by talking about "truth" and "demonstration" as if they were something apart from ourselves, so that nothing of ourselves is at stake in the outcome. We do talk about scientific demonstration in these terms: here is an interesting phenomenon, an organism to be identified, a disease to be diagnosed, an array of spots on an X-ray film to be interpreted as a broken bone or as the atomic structure of a crystal, and it makes no difference to the judge as a person which way the decision goes. We can talk about religion in the same way, as if it made no difference whether we were ourselves religious. We can talk about God as if he were one among other beings, one alternative cause among other causes explaining the national tragedy of the Hebrew people. But by this process the substance of religious events disappears because by confining them to merely external occurrences from which our own responsive participation has been excluded, we have dissolved the events of biblical religion.

For this reason, the most difficult questions we face are religious ones, and the Easter event will be the supreme difficulty, because here the act of response in commitment becomes inescapable, and we confront the inexorable fact that all demonstration rests upon the commitment to accept certain kinds of data as evidence. We must believe in order to know.

We cannot demonstrate the actuality of the Easter event—meaning now the whole complex of meanings woven about it by the Christian community of believers—to one who is unprepared to find in that event the meaning of his own existence. Neutral, impartial, disinterested demonstration of the resurrection cannot be achieved. The most we can accomplish in these terms is to show that there was a group who held certain beliefs. Whether their belief is true we cannot know or demonstrate until we also share it as our own. Then we discover that having come to share this belief, we are persuaded of its truth, and that the process cannot be reversed: knowledge cannot be prior to belief. We become a believer (the Bible says this is the work of the Holy Spirit) and in the light of this new understanding discover that our experience and our world make sense, and we have the ground upon which to invite others to share with us the light we have found. Moreover, it must be said that he who refuses to believe until the truth has been demonstrated has not taken the better or the securer road. He also is a believer—in something else.

AUTHORITY AND AUTHORITIES

ONE of the most popular religious heresies today is the notion that religion is a matter of private opinion, specifically that one is free to interpret Christian teachings as he chooses and to make the Bible say whatever he wants it to say. Many people mistakenly think that this kind of individualism in religion is the hallmark of Protestantism. This heresy of religious individualism is fed, but is in no sense verified, by the actual diversity of religious beliefs and lack of agreement on standards by which to judge.

One standard, however, is clear: in biblical religion there is no such thing as a solitary Christian, if by solitary we mean that belief and truth are interior, private, or individualistic matters. This intrinsically communal character of Christianity is asserted in a claim many people find offensive, namely, that there is no salvation outside the church. While there may be no justification for sectarianism in the Bible, no one can be a solitary participant in biblical religion.

From its beginning, biblical religion has been the faith of a community of persons who understood themselves to have been gathered as a people by God. The covenant was established between God and people, not between God and isolated individuals, one by one. That understanding continues with equal strength and vitality in Christianity. Personal responsibility for responding to God's action always means the responsibility to respond within and as a member of a community of believers, because the character of God's action in Christ is to create a people, and not simply to rescue individuals.

The Christian's understanding of the nature of man denies that the person is sovereign over himself in the sense that he is free to set his own destiny without regard to the community of faith. His commitment as a Christian believer sets him within the community of believers God has created, as one who is subject to their guidance, challenge, and support. By becoming a Christian believer, he relinquishes his autonomy and his right to make his decisions without reference to the Christian community. All his actions and his judgments must be made as one who is subject to the authority of this community, and the life and judgment of the community are subject to the authority of God's will revealed in Christ.

The use of the term "authority" can be misleading. When, in the context of biblical religion, the statement is made that the Christian lives "under authority," it does not mean that he is subject to a coercive formula, imposed by fiat and enforced by fear, which forbids the right or possibility of independent and responsible thought. Instead, the phrase properly refers to the fact that the Christian has freely and deliberately embraced a standard which he did not invent, but which he found persuasive when he saw it in action, and he employs this standard in measuring his own and the community's life. His authorities, then, consist of those standards or sources of teaching to which he appeals in order to show that his judgment is not a private predilection, but represents the authentic experience of the community in its covenant dialogue with God.

The Christian's appeal to authority, therefore, does

not represent an appeal to power, or to the mere wishes of an individual, or to the habitual prejudices of a segment of the community. There are indeed authorities in biblical religion, but their use is not an exercise of compulsion and, without turning biblical religion into a valley of dry bones, they cannot be used as fixed laws to guarantee the truth or as shortcuts to resolve the dilemma of judgment.

All forms of authority to which appeal can be made in biblical religion have arisen within the life of the biblical community of faith, as symbols of the experience of the community of faith. The Christian is obedient to them in recognition that he does respond to something outside himself and greater than himself or his private sentiments. These authorities carry conviction; they rest upon conviction; they elicit conviction in response, and they have authority because the believer has responded by accepting their jurisdiction over him. Because these authorities stand within the community of faith, in the largest sense the authority is the community itself, "spread out through all time and space and rooted in eternity, terrible as an army with banners."[8] More precisely, the authority is the faith of the community as it has been recorded in the Bible and the creeds, in the teachings of the fathers, in the decisions and pronouncements of the churches, and in the liturgies of worship. All these constitute the tradition by which the churches today, and the present generation of Christians, measure the life of the covenant community.

The Bible: Among these authorities, the Bible is most conspicuous. Its authority flows from the response of faith out of which, and to which, it speaks. Those who

[8] C. S. Lewis, *The Screwtape Letters* (New York: Macmillan, 1943), p. 15.

wrote the biblical words testify to the acts of God in which they found the meaning of their lives and proclaim that they have witnessed and shared God's work to redeem Israel and through Christ the whole world. God still speaks through their words as the reader finds himself addressed by this message of salvation and discovers himself required to answer. The biblical writers announce acts of God which were specific events in history, but the meaning of these acts and words is not to be confined to those specific times and places. "Come follow me" was not spoken by Jesus only to the first generation of disciples. Paul's experience provides the clue. As "one born out of due time" who had not known Jesus in the flesh, he found himself directly called to respond, and his career as a Christian missionary resulted. Jesus' discourses in the Fourth Gospel may not be tape recordings of his speeches, but they make the point no less clearly: he is the light of the world; he is the way to the Father; he is the good shepherd; he is the door of the sheepfold; he alone is the one through whom men come to the Father. Those today who hear these words addressed to themselves are those who find the Bible authoritative, for its authority is grounded in its direct address to the reader, who by his response becomes not only a hearer but also a participant in the story.

Yet the biblical story is not a timeless cosmic drama which can be set in any age because it belongs to none. The Bible's authority is rooted in the soil tilled by the archeologist's spade, but its authority does not stand or fall with the sifting of that soil to determine whether Jesus spoke these given words or others, or to establish which of the apostles wrote the epistles gathered in the New Testament. As has been pointed out earlier, the

Bible clearly reflects the cultural circumstances of its writers, because the response of faith must be made within the concrete texture of one's own time and place. Any proclamation of the meaning of life must be made from within some specific cultural form, and the culture of the biblical writers differed vastly from our own. Their language borrowed freely from the traditions of their neighbors in order to interpret God's acts and their relationship to him. But they transmuted these borrowings into an unquenchable assertion of God's mighty acts. However clearly the pattern of their story may be identified in the legends they appropriated, its content is their own experience as the object of God's creative and redemptive concern which embraces the whole career of man from the creation of the world to the culmination at the end of the age when the promised Kingdom will come in its fullness for all who have responded faithfully.

Despite the obvious cultural conditioning that shines through the biblical story, the Christian community has elected to make this record normative for the response in faith of succeeding generations. And rather than being embarrassed by this cultural legacy, the Christian community today sees in it the concrete historical roots from which it has grown. It nourishes itself on the faith and understanding of the apostolic community, and this apostolic experience remains authoritative for Christianity today precisely because of its historical actuality. The Bible therefore is normative because it communicates the apostolic faith to us and makes our community of faith continuous with theirs. This does not mean that we leap straight out of the twentieth century into the first and ignore the history of the Christian community which has cherished the Bible, found its life renewed by the Bible, and has handed it on to us. Nevertheless, the Bible is normative for in it the Word of God is proclaimed. We are brought into the community by hearing and receiving that Word which is declared to us as God in the person of Christ speaks to us from the biblical narrative. The degree to which we respond by identifying ourselves with that community of believers which has transmitted the Bible to us is the measure of the Bible's authority for us.

The Bible is the primary authority for Christianity because in it and through it one is confronted by God in Christ as in no other piece of writing. Therefore, some have concluded that God himself must have dictated its words. No such literalistic, if not magical and unhistorical, view of the text can effectively sustain the Bible's authority. This view only removes it—and God—from history. In fact, however, the Bible reaffirms the reality of history, not only by reflecting that history in its own words, but also by holding before the reader the events and proclamation from which Christian history flows.

By re-presenting the initial events, the Word, the Bible challenges every generation to measure its own faith and response by that of the apostolic community, and Christianity has consistently maintained that any view which contradicts or fails to coinhere with that biblical pattern of meaning must be rejected. This does not mean that the entire vocabulary of contemporary Christianity, and specifically that of formal theological discourse, must be found within the Bible. Nor does this mean that the Bible gives us a table of organization for the church, or the last word on sexual ethics, or a blueprint for the political and economic structure of our society, or even a compendium of sermon outlines for preaching. It does mean that any idea claiming to be Christian must be congruent with the insights and life of the apostolic community which created the Bible for Christianity. The Bible stands as the chief authority for identifying and discriminating ideas and experiences and policies purporting to be Christian.

The biblical test, however, is not constituted by the words of the text, but by the Word of God, the action of God proclaimed in Christ who is the Word. The words of the text must always be tested by the Word as received and responded to by the believer and the community of faith. Since the Bible coinheres with the faithful response of the community, the biblical statements do not of themselves prove, in some neutral and universal manner, that God has acted and does act in a certain way. To put this in another way: the Bible does not remove the tension of judgment in which the person and community must take the responsibility for what he and they believe, but instead initiates the tension by calling for a decision from its readers and hearers. Thus, use of the Bible as an authority involves the believer's participation in the community of faith, and specifically his response to the Christ event as God's word to man. The character of the Bible as a book of faith establishes its specific authority for Christianity—and renders the test it makes ineluctably ambiguous in use, for the Word is an action responded to, a relationship participated in, not a static doctrine or final definition.

The Christ Event is the total experience of personal meeting with Jesus Christ, involving both the Jesus of history who lived and worked in Palestine, and the resurrected Christ, who is the continuing power and presence sustaining the Christian community. This event cannot be reduced to a clear, neutral formula. The Christ event is not the words of Jesus, or the external facts about the man. It is the relationship initiated and sustained through Christ, and it cannot be confined to the Jesus of history, as if we could have the full and universal truth if we could recover the facts about him which all historians would accept. The Christ event is more than the man of the first century; it includes everything that can be identified with the experience of him in the continuing Christian community. It is the Easter story as well as the earthly career symbolized by the Sermon on the Mount. The Christ of faith is the Lord, resurrected in testimony of God's victory over sin and death, yet he is not a mere object of belief, and still less the colorless affirmation that indeed a dead man had come to life again. He is the source of the life of the Christian community; he is the power by which the Christian community lives; and he is the continuing presence in the life of the community.

Without the Christ of faith, resting upon the Easter story, the existence and survival of the Christian community cannot be explained. This does not mean that the mere survival of Christian churches into the twentieth century, not to mention the appearance of new forms of Christianity, proves that the Easter story is true. Instead, the Christian community has lived in the power of the conviction that the story is true, that the spirit of the risen Christ is in its midst, and it attributes its activity and the resurgence of faith and renewal of its life to the working of Christ's spirit among its members.

When the Christ event includes the whole transaction of this community of faith, focussed in the life, death, and resurrection of Jesus Christ, accompanied by the conviction that the risen Christ continues to dwell within his church, it becomes clear that no purely physical facts about an empty tomb or the characteristics of a resurrected body can carry the freight of its meaning. The Christ event cannot be reduced to a test oath formula, for this would produce only verbal orthodoxy. Not even the assertions of the creeds will serve. They only symbolize, they do not capture or define the vitality of the response to Christ in which the community lives.

It would be more accurate to say that the Christ event marks the standard, the goal, rather than serves as a rule by which to test divergencies from authentic practice or quality of life or understanding of the meaning of man before God. The Christ event cannot be reduced to this kind of a rule to measure orthodoxy. The reality of the Christ event lives in the vibrant relationship of the community of faith where men are redeemed from predation and exploitation into a supporting participation in one another's lives. If this experience is rare, it is not because it is a delusion, or because we cannot measure it, or recognize its coming, or identify its lapse. It is rare because the churches fall visibly and undeniably short of what they know their life should be, and this occurs because they have failed to test themselves by the Christ event, preferring instead the patterns of tradition or verbal orthodoxy or the norms of secular society. We can say this only if we admit that the tests embodied in the Christ event at work in the life of the community are effective to identify the quality and the extent of the Christian community.

The life of the churches stands under the judgment of Christ for their failure to incarnate and to communicate the life of reconciliation from God in Christ in which they were created. This is why the churches stand condemned in the declaration that they are among the most racially segregated institutions in our society. Just as one can recognize that new quality of reconciled life within himself and among others, he can identify its absence or its denial. A dramatic application of this test propels the ecumenical movement. Despite the real and very human dangers of a superchurch and an ecclesiastical bureaucracy, the ecumenical movement moves by the power of the realization that in Christ, God has declared and generated a reconciling activity to create unity among men which the churches still resist and resent by cherishing their institutional autonomies.

Unity, which is the fruit of biblical religion, is not to be defined as uniformity, but as the coinherence of diversities. The boundaries of the unity created by the reconciling work of God in Christ cannot be set with clear precision, and participation in the life of the community of faith confers no release from the uncertainty and ambiguity of judgment. The mark of the truth is finally the character proclaimed for the people God creates. If his work is reconciliation, then the mark of its fulfillment among his people is unity among the reconciled. By no means, however, does the mark of unity become a diffuse and vague remark about life in general. It becomes the specific and concrete claim that a community of reconciliation does exist, and its sign is the unity known by participating in its life.

The pressure for uniformity comes from the very human fact that the only secure and neutral definition of unity we possess is uniformity of idea and practice, the identity produced by conformity to a common pattern. Against this monotonous regularity stands true unity as that foundation of shared purpose, mutual understanding, and common values which delights in difference, and revels in the exchange that comes only from difference. The bond of this unity sustains difference, even when impatience or limited understanding or curdled sympathy turns diversity into disagreement and difference into strife. Within the bond of unity, which transcends divergent views, truth is appropriated, and in its light errors are uncovered and corrected.

How are errors corrected within the bond of unity? By discovering that our fellows will neither accept the interpretation we offer and the action it implies, nor let us go our own way alone. They cannot agree with us, but they will not abandon us to the solitariness of our error. As each person finds himself in turn the beneficiary of this relationship which sustains while it challenges, and supports while it corrects, he grows in his power to understand, to contribute to, and to receive from the personal interaction which constitutes the community. In the fullest sense of the term, this is the life and the work of Christian love released within the community of faith, and flowing from it out into the larger, secular community. One can recognize the working of this relationship in himself, and he can know it in his fellows. By it he knows forgiveness and reconciliation. In this exchange, which disciplines and selects and chastens, all the possibilities of error or perversion, all the glories and subtleties of individual insight and response, flow together to make the common life and action of the community.

This kind of community of reconciliation is what

Christians believe the church is intended to be, because the church exists from, and lives by the Spirit of Christ in its midst. And they believe that where this kind of community does exist, it has been created in their midst by the action of God. They did not themselves create it, because they believe it transcends the capacity of man—limited as he is by sin—to achieve, and one's elemental response when this community reaches out to bring him in is not necessarily an enthusiastic welcoming of the changes it brings within oneself. When the church is spoken of as the People of God or the Body of Christ, the meaning in these words is the actuality of God's reconciling activity in Christ to create a co-inherent community which communicates authentic reconciliation among men.

Why, then, are there so many churches, and how does one recognize the true church? There are many churches because, again and again, unity in the Spirit has been constricted into submission to some external formula, and in response to that demand for conformity, some Christians have been impelled to resist it in the name of the integrity of their own response to God's spirit. In other instances, men have cherished their own views in preference to the discipline of participation in a community. Who is correct? The biblical view of man reminds us that since we all are sinners, none of the contending views or dissident parties or specific institutions is wholly right, because no person or position or institution escapes the dilemma of judgment in human existence.

The normal, ordinary life of man falls far short of unity in exchange. Instead of seeking reconciliation by welcoming the challenge of those who differ with us, we confine our relationships to those with whom we agree because they are like ourselves. Being what we are, we cannot live alone, but neither can we live with our fellows in the joy of exchange. The Christian claim is that the work of God in Christ was, and is, to heal the brokenness of our relations with our fellows, so that our necessarily social nature will express and fulfill the life for which we were made.

The degree of truth attained within the community is measured by the patience and persistence of its individual members in obedience to the community, and by the whole community's receptiveness to the insights of its individual members. Within the community of reconciliation, unity is not compromise, but the discovery of that understanding and relationship which is broad enough and compelling enough to enlist the loyalty and to support the participation of all. Such unity, Christians believe, is beyond the power of unaided men to achieve; it comes only from the continued presence of Christ within the community of believers. His work of reconciliation required his crucifixion, and it may demand the same of those who follow him.

The Christian says that while this unity in community is the work of God, it does not and cannot give him the certainty of final proof. Such certainty can be obtained only by denying his dialogue with God. What unity does give is the assurance of participating in a community that is grounded in the acts of God, and the courage to be a person under God. Beyond this participation we can achieve no purer preception and possess no greater certainty.

In the end, all tests of truth, all attempts to prove the truth of the Christian claims, must be unsatisfactory to the scientific mind. Scientific demonstration of the historical facts about the career of Jesus or the biblical tradition cannot reach to the heart of personal response which makes that tradition authentic. A decision to participate or to reject it is required, and this must be the action of a person. And he cannot confine his judgment by setting up an external, neutral standard for the faith by which he lives. There are standards in biblical religion, but they are guides for action, not boundaries upon the truth; they are counsels of perfection, not scientific laws for the spiritual world; and they function in the life of the community itself. In biblical religion, proof ultimately consists of the shared experience which comes in the discovery that the meaning for one's own existence is also the meaning in which his fellows live. It is the creation of unity in purpose and spirit, of harmony in action, of concord in vision, of participation and support in the web of exchange. That is, proof belongs to the coinherence of life.

Our nature as persons prohibits us from achieving a proof that can be certain beyond all doubt. Men march to the beat of many different drums, but the Christian believes that there is a truth in relationship embracing us all, and therefore there is the hope of unity with those who disagree and who find other meanings in our common world. Coherence, unity in exchange, lives of coinherence in exchange: these are the clues by which we measure truth; these are the foundation of proof in the community of biblical faith, and also, as we shall see in succeeding chapters, in the community of science as well.

Part Three ✸

SCIENCE

Chapter Five ✱

THE ART OF SCIENCE

Then I saw that wisdom excels folly as light excels darkness. The wise man has his eyes in his head, but the fool walks in darkness. ECCLESIASTES 2:13–14

THE PERSON IN SCIENCE

BECAUSE science answers the question, "What?" many people believe that science cleaves the horns of the dilemma which plainly confronts us in religion. They expect scientific knowledge to give so clear a description of the conditions under which we live that our course of action will then be equally clearly indicated. They assume science to be a self-moving and self-directing enterprise that provides definitive knowledge on any topic, as if the words "scientifically proved" banished all further questions and made any personal commitment unnecessary. Both our willingness to alter our behavior in response to new information about our world, and the overwhelming commitment to scientific ways of thought in our culture, contribute to this mistaken impression that science is autonomous and self-correcting, and that scientific results are self-evidently true for everyone. Many scientists themselves hold this notion, and they express it in the frequent assertion that scientists can prove their claims, while religious claims cannot be proved.

We are slowly coming to see, however, that since science is an activity of persons, it does not obviate the problem of judgment but illustrates it. While the scientist works within a formal structure, the structure does not function by itself. It is operated by men who work with it and decide what to do with it. Although we systematize our knowledge of the external world, and emphasize training for research, we are beginning to appreciate that scientific discovery is itself an art, not a science. There are no scientific rules for scientific discovery. Often the conventional five-step description of scientific method as several stages of observing and hypothesizing has given the impression that these steps are a recipe for scientific discovery. But there are no standard patterns for constructing fruitful hypotheses, or for designing significant experiments. Instrumental observers cannot replace human observers (on the moon, for example) for the simple reason that human beings have imagination; they envisage goals; therefore they can determine which phenomena are significant despite the fact that they do not have and cannot be given prior instructions on what to look for. Instruments can observe with unwavering fidelity and unblinking concentration what they have been programmed to look for, and because they have no initiative, they will see nothing else. Like stupid servants, they will follow precisely the instructions they have been given, rather than the intention which lay behind the instructions.

Computers have vastly increased our power to analyze complex arrays of data to make them yield significant patterns. The definition of significance, however, has to be programmed into the computer by the scientist who decides what the computer shall do. To take a single example: a computer was programmed to analyze the patterns in human brain waves in order to determine whether responses to known stimuli could be identified in what appears to be a continuous flow of seemingly random electrical currents in the brain cortex. The computer was instructed to watch for and average together instances of a certain kind of repeated pattern, while ignoring everything else within the complex flow of waves. Because of its highly selective attention and its infallible memory, it would not be misled by dramatic but irregular and irrelevant peaks in the current flow. But "in applying this technique the neuro-physiologist must necessarily make certain assumptions about the character of the biological phenomena he regards as signal and that which he chooses to call noise."[1] The computer can find patterns in what looks like chaos, once it has been told what it is to regard as pattern. It cannot decide whether there is a pattern to be looked for, or what characteristics would define a pattern. Here the person of the scientist enters, and there is no formal or scientific means to determine whether the pattern chosen as the signal is really more significant than what is being rejected as noise. This becomes a matter of personal judgment.

It can be said, of course, that this choice is validated if fruitful results follow. Again judgment enters to define fruitfulness. What is fruitful depends in the end

[1] Mary A. B. Brazier, "The Analysis of Brain Waves," *Scientific American,* Vol. 206, No. 6 (June, 1962), p. 144.

upon the purposes of the scientist himself. The claim that fruitfulness is measured by whether the results contribute to further scientific activity does not eliminate the scientist's responsibility for judgment. This only says that the scientist has decided that more scientific knowledge is itself the goal. It is perfectly legitimate for the scientist to say that he is curious, and that he wants to see what happens when "this" is mixed with "that," or what "this" will do under "those" conditions. The point remains that even when his reasons are as local as these—or as earth-shaking, when "this" is a nuclear bomb—there are no scientific criteria or impersonal standards to which he can appeal to justify his decision. Scientific activity is not self-justifying. It is the product of a commitment that is made by persons and societies.

THE SCIENTIFIC COMMUNITY

THE human and personal side of science appears no less clearly in a social form. Science is not a solitary activity. It is an activity of a community in several different ways, and one of the more trivial of these is the fact that more and more research is being done by teams rather than by individual workers. Team research may represent no more than the fact that much modern equipment is too complex for one person to handle by himself. But a deeper significance lies in team research. Dean Harold K. Schilling of Pennsylvania State University is fond of asking unwary Ph.D. candidates if a single skilled scientist, given time and unlimited access to equipment, could by himself build up the present body of scientific knowledge. It is tempting to say yes, since with unlimited access to computers, and all the time one needs, an enormous amount of research work could be done.

However, the correct answer is no, because the scientist needs the interaction with his fellows, both to stimulate and to support his own personal activity, and to correct his mistakes by challenging his ideas.

The solitary scientist would go mad, not necessarily from loneliness, but from paranoia. He would have no way of learning where his interpretations were warped and mistaken. The world itself could not set him right, because nature does not provide us with the safe or proper questions to ask. His computers could not tell him, because he programmed them. Only other persons, acting from their own responsible commitments, can flag his errors and force him to reconsider his interpretation of the data, because they find other meanings in the phenomena than those which he sets forth. This is the profit from professional meetings and from publication.

The scientific community has both formal and informal ways of recognizing achievement, and of correcting errors of judgment and interpretation. The most formal is the structure of scientific reasoning itself, and every scientific claim must meet this test. This is supposed to be the test applied by the referees for scientific journals when papers are submitted to them to decide whether they merit publication, and this is the test one invites by publishing his results. This is the test applied when other scientists attempt to reproduce the results reported by an investigator.

Nonetheless, the formality and rigor of scientific reasoning does not in itself yield hard and fast lines by which to identify competent scientific work or to define scientific truth. In principle, both the evidence and the process of reasoning erected around the evidence are publicly available to all persons in the same fashion.

But no matter how impeccable, no evidence or line of reasoning that fails to win the assent of the total community will be accepted as part of the growing structure of scientific knowledge.

The fabric of knowledge in science is the creation of a community, and the assurance of any one person about the validity and viability of his own work requires that it be accepted by his co-workers. The fact that this process of judgment is a community function does not make it into a purely formal and neutral criterion, and the process does not become infallible because many persons participate in it. Instead, scientists trust one another to detect and correct indvidual errors and to affirm correct judgements, and in the end they are compelled to trust each other because no criteria of truth are self-applying. Every formal pattern of reasoning is no more than a pattern for thinking which must always be carried through by persons, and there is no reason to expect that every person who uses the pattern will see the world in the same way.

The suggestion is sometimes made that the scientist's commitment to honest reporting of his data is the key factor in the scientific process. In one sense this is the case, because no scientist has time to repeat everything for himself to make sure that the record has not been falsified. Dishonest reporting, however, is not so much a sin against science as it is against the community of scientists. Mistakes can be corrected, and there is no formal difference between a human being's mistakes and a computer's occasional errors. But there is a vast difference in the significance of such errors when they can be identified as intentional falsification. A scientist's career is destroyed completely if it becomes known that he falsely reported an experiment or permitted a student under his guidance to falsify his results.

Although it is the presumption of scientific activity that we all confront the same world, and that the ultimate appeal is to some event in that world, the understanding of that world, which we accept as scientific knowledge, has been created by the participation and interaction of the members of the scientific community. Each person relies on this body of accumulated results because he assumes that every person who has participated in creating it has acted with as full a sense of responsibility as himself. The one who falsifies his results has therefore betrayed this trust. The odd result is that it is not nearly so much the world that guarantees the truth of scientific knowledge, as it is our mutual trust in each other as persons of integrity. What purports to be a neutral and impersonal description of the world of natural events around us, turns out to be dependable because we can trust one another. Without abrogating any of the scientist's insistence that events in the external world are the final appeal, making that appeal is a human and social enterprise. The evidential value of any event in the external world is finally a value given to it by some person's interpretation made in interaction with, and supported by, the judgments of his fellows.

Informal methods of judgment are no less effective than formal reasoning, and are more interesting because here the scientist as a person appears more clearly. A devastating question for a brilliant and articulate physical chemist during his Ph.D. oral examination is to ask him what chemistry is, and specifically to require that he differentiate his activity in physical chemistry from physics. He knows that there is a difference because he is getting his degree in physical chemistry, not physics. Nonetheless, the most he can say is that he approaches problems in chemical terms, while the physicist would use physical terms in dealing with the same problem. Just what the difference between chemical and physical terms is he cannot precisely say. The scientists on the examining committee know what he means, but they are little more successful than he in stating the difference. They want to say more than "chemistry is what we do in this building, while physics is what physicists do next door." They have a feeling for what chemical activity properly is, and they share this recognition with their fellow chemists. That is why they are chemists. They recognize in each other and in each other's work a point of view common to all chemists, and a common approach to problems, a shared understanding in chemical terms of what the world is and how it goes. They have spent their professional careers becoming habituated to this way of responding to the world and to this way of interpreting the phenomena they explore. They feel it in their bones, and if someone else does not feel it in his, he simply is not a member of the chemical community, and there are no words or formal concepts which will of themselves initiate him into the community.

In chemistry, as well as in other areas, formal definitions do not help very much. By the time one is able to frame for his activity a formal definition which clearly distinguishes its unique features from similar activities, he has long since passed the point where he needs such definitions, and those who stand outside can make little use of the definition because it awakens no echoes in their own pattern of understanding and response. It is as true in chemistry as in religion that one can genuinely understand only from inside the community.

A similar process, largely inarticulate if not unconscious, operates to identify the scientist whose words carry no weight and whose papers do not secure publication or a hearing at professional meetings. His ideas, his way of construing experience, do not quite harmonize with those of the rest of the scientific community, even though he uses the same formal pattern of reasoning. His conclusions, if not his premises, do not display the same pattern of events that the rest recognize. The data take a different meaning in his hands. The same awareness of a shared understanding explains the reports of scientists that they frequently find it easier to communicate with fellow scientists across national, political, and language barriers than they do to communicate with their own compatriots in a different line of work.

THE SCIENTIFIC COMMITMENT

BECAUSE its members share a common commitment, a scientific community does exist, and does transcend national and language boundaries. To a greater extent than most of us appreciate, the basic premises of this commitment have permeated our culture beyond the limits of the professional scientific community, so that it has become self-evident that all except a few vagrant problems—as perhaps those of art—ought to be approached in a scientific spirit. Our age is properly called "The Age of Science" because of this tacit *intention* to be scientific. And we are so bemused by the technological virtuosity of science that we have lost sight of it as an intention.

Our age is not a scientific age because we have a heliocentric cosmology, while an earlier age was unscientific because it still held that the earth was at the center of things. Attitude, not content, is the defining criterion, and the essential attitude in the scientific commitment is that the answer to the question of "What?" requires as clear and distinct a separation between the phenomena we are observing, and ourselves as observers as can be accomplished. The scientific answer requires that the external world be described in impersonal terms independently of human concerns or presence or participation.

In fields like physics and chemistry, this attitude of detachment seems almost inevitable and is easy to attain in practice because the experimental material evinces no consciousness and its processes occur without exhibiting awareness of the experimenter. In the life sciences, a clear separation of this kind is not so easy to attain, and in the behavioral sciences, especially where the phenomenon is human behavior, a conscious and strenuous effort at detachment is required to maintain the essential separation between the observer and the phenomena he describes.[2]

Phenomena are to be interpreted as interactions of physical forces and bodies, occurring without consciousness or sense of direction, having no goal, and experiencing no joy or sadness on the way, because such personal responses represent the intrusion of our own psychic life into the process of energy exchanges. Such emotional projections have no place in a scientific account of physical-chemical changes because they are not accessible to the instruments or conceptual tools we use to deal with physical-chemical events.

Any observable phenomenon which can be treated in these impersonal, detached terms, can become a part of the scientific picture of our world. What cannot be observed and treated in these impersonal terms cannot

[2] Cf. Leslie H. Farber, "'I'm Sorry, Dear,'" *Commentary*, Vol. 38, No. 5 (Nov., 1964), pp. 47–54.

be part of a scientific picture or invoked as a scientific explanation.[3] Sometimes this limitation is stated as the requirement that science is restricted to secondary causes. The term "secondary cause" refers to those factors which are intrinsic to the situation and are capable of observation, in contrast to ultimate or first causes or impalpable factors lying beyond the reach of experimental control or observation. No scientific explanation can be achieved by appealing to factors which cannot themselves be investigated by the same techniques that are used elsewhere in the situation under study. In other words, the intention is to produce a closed system of interpretation.

A corollary of the restriction to secondary causes is the restriction against multiplying explanations. If one cause is a sufficient explanation, additional explanatory principles are unnecessary. Nothing is gained by adding God or other immaterial entities to a scientific explanation. However, this restriction does not mean that science shows God to be unnecessary, but only that God does not belong in a scientific account of the character of events in the world.

Corresponding to the intention to describe a world in impersonal terms is the conception of what constitutes an authentic event in that world. An event, in scientific terms, must be an observable change in state or place which would be equally accessible to any observer. According to this definition, when two people disagree, at least one has made an observational error—because the world is the same for both, and equally available to both, the truth about it must also be the same. No event will be admitted as authentic in a scientific account which

[3] Cf. B. F. Skinner, "Behaviorism at Fifty," *Science,* Vol. 140, No. 3570 (May 31, 1963), pp. 951–958.

only one or a few exceptional persons could observe. Here is the difficulty with psychic phenomena such as mental telepathy or precognition or telekinesis. If these "events" occur as the kind of events they are claimed to be, they occur under special circumstances associated with particular individuals who apparently possess extraordinary capacities. They cannot be made uniformly available to all observers. The specific problem of evidence in scientific historiography is the problem of making sure that the data offered about any purported event are of a kind equally available to all observers, so that an impartial decision is possible. Among the kinds of evidence which meet the requirement are such things as an impersonal change of state, a meter reading, a measurement, an artifact, a document, a concrete object.

When persons and personal relationships are set within this impersonal and impartial interpretive pattern, they necessarily lose their personal character and content. The scientific treatment of man means that one deals with persons and their purposes in the same fashion that one deals with phenomena or beings which exhibit no consciousness or purpose, that is, one confines himself to behavior, and he does not consider attitudes or purposes or emotional responses. Of course one may investigate these as aspects *of* behavior, but the scientist reports what the subject does in overt action, not what the investigator presumes the subject was feeling, thinking about, or intending. This does not mean that in order to be scientific one must deny that persons exist. On the contrary it does mean that one is being unscientific if he permits the qualities of personal action and appropriation to affect his work or his interpretation. To be scientific is to eliminate oneself as completely as possible from the total interaction, so that one produces as pure an account of the "what" confronting him as can be obtained. Intentionally, one's participation as a person is reduced and made subject to the demand for an impartial account of observable events.

This goal itself, however, is a human value, representing the tacit if not explicit agreement of the scientific community to work in this fashion toward this end. It does not follow that the truest picture of the world has no man in it. Instead, it follows from this goal that the scientific picture is designed to exclude the personal action of such beings by subsuming all events under general and impersonal patterns of relationship stated as laws.

Given such an intention, expressed in the requirement that only observable events which are common to all observers can be counted as relevant data or evidence, it follows inevitably that many aspects of human experience fall under a cloud when treated scientifically. Consequently, many people have concluded that science is appropriate only for certain kinds of phenomena, namely, physical and quantifiable ones, while human responsiveness, as in religion, or art, or politics, requires some other kind of knowledge. Actually, however, the limits of scientific knowledge are set by the kind of answer desired rather than by the kind of phenomenon under scrutiny. The answer incarnated in scientific practice is that which is identical for all persons because it is stated in the neutral terms of measurements and laws of interaction between impersonal entities. Truth and falsity in scientific terms thus become matters to be decided by impartial evidence. Truth of this kind about religion, politics, art, and other areas of human experience and expression, not excluding the most intimate aspects of sexual experience, is possible to attain. Only sometimes we permit ourselves to forget our prior decision to seek this kind of truth in these neutral and formal terms.

Chapter Six ✸

THE WEIGHT OF EVIDENCE

And the Lord said to Moses, "How long will this people despise me? And how long will they not believe in me, in spite of all the signs which I have wrought among them?"
NUMBERS 14:11

THE SHAPE OF SCIENTIFIC KNOWLEDGE

THE INTENTION to be scientific in the pursuit of knowledge does not operate in a vacuum. We do not receive the phenomena of the world entirely free from preconceptions, or from expectations as to what we will find there or how we will understand the data that we observe. These expectations form the framework of our thought by which we organize our experience, and, rather than exhibiting the self-evidently rational character of the universe, they are the implicit ground rules by which we think. They determine the direction we will look for explanations, and they provide the usually unstated but controlling conditions which explanations must meet if they are to be accepted as satisfactory.

Most laymen still picture the world as a Newtonian,

machine-like universe of colliding, solid particles, moving in a Euclidean three-dimensional space. In such a world, things have definite internal natures and strictly defined boundaries, and their connections with each other are as fixed as in a system of gears and levers so that events have precisely identifiable causes, and events are adequately explained when their causes have been ascertained. Although in formal work in the physical sciences, quantum mechanics and relativity theory have replaced the rigidity and simplicity of this Newtonian world-machine, it still influences our thinking, for we have not begun seriously to think of things as bundles of energy and of the interactions and dynamic balance of fields of force, but prefer to think in terms of the mechanical impacts of determinate objects, even when we are considering the behavior of human beings. For example, those who talk of a natural economic law of supply and demand are trying to describe a Newtonian economic pattern.

Outside the physics laboratory, the implications of relativity theory have penetrated only dimly, if at all, and then primarily in the guise of the grossly mistaken notion that it implies moral relativism. One reason for the persistence of the Newtonian world-machine model, aside from its attractively simplistic kind of truth, may be that in modern physics and chemistry, visual models for the most part are eschewed in favor of mathematical formulae which convey nothing to the mind of the uninitiated. Among recent scientific advances, evolutionary ideas have permeated widely enough beyond their specifically biological base to become a popular model of explanation. In its terms, there is a law of progress; complexity equals improvement; the newest and most elaborate is of the highest value, and antiquity denotes the crude, the primitive, the simple, and the naive.

Such over-simple, mechanistic pictures as these no longer serve the needs of scientific work, just as we now know that the familiar solar system picture of atomic structure is no longer adequate. In them, however, we can see the underlying presumption of scientific knowledge, namely, that we are dealing with a universe, not a multiverse. This means that we expect to find the same system of processes and relationships operating throughout the experienced world, so that the entire natural order constitutes a single order, exhibiting everywhere the same principles at work. We expect to find a coherent universe, and coherent means that there exists only one system of principles and relationships, not several. The presence of incompatible systems of interaction and relationship would be incoherent because they could not be fitted together to form one pattern. Our insistence that the truth must be the same for all observers is an example of the demand for coherence. In other words, we do not accept special explanations for special situations, because this would mean the existence of several incompatible and disconnected sets of operating principles. For the same reason, we restrict explanations to the simplest form. Additional explanatory principles are suspect more because they raise the possibility of incoherence, than because they are superfluous.

While this may seem too obvious to deserve mention, we need to remind ourselves that we have not *proved* that the world is a single system of principles and relationships. On the contrary, we have *presumed* this to be the case, and we have constructed our knowledge of the world accordingly. Of course we expect things to make sense, and by and large, we succeed in making sense out of them. We are not content simply to accept the reality of any occurrence which we cannot fit into our total picture of the universe. Here is our problem in the recurring flurries of excitement over "unidentified flying objects." Either we investigate the situation until we discover how to fit it in, or we insist that it did not occur as reported and therefore that it does not exist (and we are skilled at pretending that factors inconvenient for our small world views do not exist). The fact that we so often do find connections between events, and thus are able to construct a single total picture, does not prove that they are all parts of the same total system. Instead, this is the descriptive goal we have set out to achieve. We need to remember that the orderliness which we find in nature and express in the structure of scientific knowledge, rests as much upon our demand for coherence as upon any intrinsic orderliness in nature itself.

The structure of scientific knowledge expresses our expectation that the world does not change in capricious or random fashion, and therefore what we experience more or less directly is representative of a whole order of nature. While we insist that conclusions should not be extended beyond the specific situation studied, no one would continue a research program for very long if he were convinced that his findings would have no relevance beyond the specific circumstances he was investigating. Actually if his findings had no relevance beyond that specific situation he could not even understand it, for we expect that the limited research area will be described and its principles of operation analyzed in such a way as to show both how this portion of experience fits into the rest of the world we know, and how our experience here will illuminate other areas of experience as yet unexamined. This is the underlying presupposition of sampling procedures. The sample actually studied is presumed to be characteristic of the whole if each member of that whole had an equal chance of being included in the sample under investigation. Such a sampling process can be extended by constructing typical samples that are miniature models of the whole, and on this basis public opinion polls seem to be able to assess such opinions as voting preferences with high accuracy from very small sample groups.

The idea that the forces and processes we see operating in the given situation extend throughout time and space was formalized in geology a century ago by Sir Charles Lyell as the doctrine of uniformitarianism. Without this principle, all predictions of the future or accounts of what has happened in the past would be quite impossible. Such sciences as astrophysics and paleontology specifically presume that the pattern or process observed in the local instance does extend to other situations in the past or future and to other regions in space. What the paleontologist has in his hand is a rock containing a fossil: a bit of petrified bone or a cast of a shell. This fragment becomes the fulcrum for a vast reconstruction of a living creature and its ecology, and the basis for a geological calendar, on the presumption that muscles have always been attached to bones in the same manner as in creatures now living, and that similar species have always required similar conditions of temperature and nourishment, and that such processes as rainfall, erosion and redeposition, and diastrophism have always functioned as they do now.

A given interpretation of the fossil or of any other specific event will be persuasive to the degree that it brings into view the operation of processes and relationships that have already been observed in other situations. Specifically, the given event or situation is considered to be explained when it can be shown to be an instance of a general principle or scientific law. We not only expect to find a single, coherent universe, we do not believe that we have the key to its coherence until we can state the operating principle or relationship in the form of a scientific law. Lacking such laws or principles, we are reduced to bare description, and apparent similarity or mere succession become the only links between events.

In current scientific practice, it is preferred that laws should be stated in mathematical form, but mathematical formulation is not the criterion. It is essential to the law that it should state the operating principle in the form of an unvarying relationship between the essential factors in the situation. The term "law" is unfortunate because its coercive and juridical connotations suggest that these "laws" are governing powers controlling the world. This flavor is especially pronounced when the phrase "natural law" is construed to mean the pattern built into the world by a Creator and imposed by him upon both nature and human thought and action. Some people still speak of "laws of nature" which cannot be violated, and there was a time when scientists thought that their "scientific laws" uncovered the hidden but actual nature of things. Scientists no longer anticipate being able to penetrate the veil which conceals fundamental essences. Now their aim is to identify the principle of interaction in functional terms by stating how one factor varies as a function of changes in the others.

It is not correct to say that a scientific law is a

generalization upon a series of observations or mass of data, even though it may have been developed as a result of a long series of specific observations. Instead, it states the functioning relationship that is identical in the varied individual instances. The law describes no particular instance. It states the essential clue in every instance of the kind. Accordingly, it is considerably more accurate to conceive of a scientific law as an idealized limit, because it states the pure case with all the qualifications and variations arising from individual circumstances eliminated.

The law is a precisely abstract statement; it refers only to the essential factors in the process, and eliminates all the irrelevant factors which inhabit every specific event. Boyle's Law provides a convenient illustration: pressure-volume ratio in a gas is a constant, given normal temperature range and a perfect gas (one for which actual measurement would give a constant ratio). Another example is the acceleration formula which reduces the essentials to distance and time. Who is falling, or why, is irrelevant. The point to a law is that it tells us what should be happening if there is nothing extraneous in the situation to twist the observed results.

As an idealized limit, a scientific law is more than just a rule of inference. It does state how we will interpret a given situation, and if the observed results do not match the pattern described by the law, we are warned to look further to discover the added factor. But we also discover that as the experimental situation is simplified to reduce more nearly to the essential stated in the law, the observed results match more closely the statement in the law.

Obviously, the goal of bringing all knowledge into

the form of law has been only partially achieved, and a law which would unite electro-magnetism and gravitation in a single system not only eluded Einstein but continued to elude his successors. There are still large areas of nature where experimentation consists frankly in fishing expeditions in search of the characteristics and properties of things under new conditions—at temperatures near absolute zero, for example. When enough data have been gathered, it may be possible to formulate the functional relationship as a law which will enable us to manipulate the phenomena to our chosen ends. In dealing with events involving human beings and their relationships, we are far from this goal: for example, no generally acceptable historical laws have been formulated as yet. If we do achieve scientific knowledge of human behavior, however, it will be in the form of such laws, precisely because this is what we mean by scientific knowledge of human behavior.

THE DETERMINISTIC CHARACTER OF SCIENTIFIC KNOWLEDGE

IT is usually assumed that scientific knowledge, stated in terms of laws, gives us a deterministic and materialistic world, and the popularity of this conclusion is not diminished by the endeavor of the behavioral scientists to develop laws covering human behavior. Many scientists believe that a deterministic world is what they have demonstrated. Many other people, motivated by humanistic and religious values, have attacked science for excluding any "spiritual" realm from consideration.

Both groups misunderstand the functional character of scientific knowledge. While some scientists indubitably are materialists and atheists, science itself is not committed to materialism as a basic premise about the ultimate nature of reality. Instead, scientific description, being limited to observed behavior, tells us nothing about ultimate essences, and unobservable entities such as "mind" or "consciousness" cannot become factors in the statement of scientific principles.

Perhaps the clearest modern definition of "matter" (and the one still most common in everyday use) was given by Thomas Hobbes, who taught that all events are due to matter in motion, and by matter, he meant some kind of solid, inert particle moved entirely by external impact. No sophisticated scientist today attributes these qualities to the "physical" stuff of the universe. The equation between matter and energy has turned the apparently solid stuff of our gross sensory experience into bundles of intricately balanced energy states. When matter thus acquires the qualities of activity which were once restricted to mind, meaningful distinctions between a "material" realm and a "mental" realm begin to fade. What the term "material" means as a working concept today is not at all clear, and scientists no longer appeal to it because their subject matter is observable events.

It is often said that science denies the presence or relevance of purpose in the world. This is correct, but not because scientists do not believe in purpose or meaning. Purpose is denied as a part of the scientific picture of the world because purpose as such can neither be observed nor brought under any kind of experimental control. We can measure with precision the strength of the electrical current in a grid required to keep a sexually deprived male white rat from approaching an estrous female white rat, and the strength of electrical shock the animal will sustain to get to the female provides an index of the strength of his sexual drive. But we are not measuring, and have no way to explore, any intention or purpose on the part of the animal. Similarly, with human subjects, it is quite easy to obtain verbal reports from them as to their intentions or purposes, but there is no way to determine the correctness of their verbal reports except by observing their behavior, and then the purely "mental" aspects of purpose have disappeared again.

No purpose or intention or goal can be identified in its own terms as an appropriate part of a scientific account. All that can be said in scientific terms is that an event occurred because the conditions of energy exchange were appropriate for it. Thus, the sexual "drive" of the white rat is an energy imbalance which sexual gratification restores. It is not possible to say that the sexual activity arose from any given purpose or that it was carried through in order to fulfill any goal beyond restoring the organism's energy balance. We, as human beings, envisage goals, and we impose these goals upon the processes of nature by building dams or by spraying insecticides or by intervening surgically, and we use our scientific knowledge to tell us where and how most effectively to intervene. However, these goals of ours are not a part of the scientific account of the processes we interfere with, and no scientifically describable goal or purpose intrinsic to those processes is served, as they submit to or frustrate our interference. So far as scientific knowledge is concerned, the processes simply proceed.

When biologists, for example, use teleological language to describe the adaptive behavior of organisms, or to identify the survival advantages of certain mutations, they deny that these words imply an intention on the part of the organism to achieve any goal by such behavior or changes in form. Equally, they deny that in scientific terms, the whole selective process of evolution can be said to serve any end, as if the survival of certain organisms rather than others were itself a goal or had meaning and value. Thus, so far as the scientific account is concerned, the survival of man cannot be said to be the goal of the evolutionary process. Protective coloration in moths is a good example of the point. In less than a century, the increase in industrial soot in England and western Europe has resulted in "industrial melanism" in many species of moths that exhibit both a light-colored form and a dark or melanic form. Where once the light forms predominated, now the majority are dark, matching the soot-darkened surfaces the moths rest on during the day. Obviously, a bird seeking food is more likely to find a white moth on soot-blackened bark than to find a dark one there, but a properly scientific account does not admit that the moths know or care what they are doing.[1] From the scientific point of view, the natural process simply is what it is; the scientist does not predicate that it has either goals or directing purpose or destination. Those who interpret evolution as a process with a direction are adding something beyond the appropriate content of science.[2]

For the same reason God must be left outside any system of scientific explanation. The reply Laplace is said to have made when Napoleon inquired why his cosmology made no reference to God, "Sire, I have no need of that hypothesis," is appropriate for any scientist with reference to scientific activity. Those Christians who urge God as an alternative explanation to replace

[1] H. D. B. Kettlewell, "Darwin's Missing Evidence," *Scientific American*, Vol. 200, No. 3 (March, 1959), pp. 48–53.

[2] Cf. Pierre Teilhard de Chardin, *The Phenomenon of Man* (New York: Harper and Row, 1959).

physical and chemical and social causes to explain natural or social processes, make a sad mistake. They are domesticating God into one cause among many, in a way that scientists properly refuse to do.

When we turn to the deterministic character, as distinguished from a supposed materialistic content, of scientific knowledge, a more viable issue arises. Scientific knowledge is necessarily deterministic, for its basic principle of explanation is deliberately limited to terms of physical forces and factors entering into the given situation. In classical physical terms, this is the billiard table universe, whose principle was also stated by Laplace, when he said that if we had precise knowledge of the position and velocity of the particles composing the universe, we could then predict accurately all future positions and velocities of these particles, and thus know exactly all the future states of the universe. Two different points are at stake. One is the view that the world is a wholly deterministic structure of events. The other is the possibility of knowing what that structure is.

Contemporary physicists now assert that the Laplacean ideal of a completely deterministic knowledge cannot be fulfilled. They are convinced that it is not possible to determine precisely both the position and the velocity of a particle. As one measurement is made more precise the other becomes less so and can only be stated as a progressively greater range of probability. With large objects such as billiard balls, projectiles, and planets, the range of probability may still fall within the diameter of the particle, and so be ignored for practical purposes. It is possible for hunters to shoot flying ducks. But with particles of electron size, the range of probability may be enormous relative to the diameter of the particle, so that a large uncertainty enters into any prediction of future states. Moreover, the very attempt to detect the location of the particle requires that we interfere with it, and we cannot know what effect our interference has made, so that at best we can only say where it was when we interfered with it, and we do not know what direction it went or where it is now. The most that we can say about the course of future events is to estimate the probability of a range of events, but this is not the Laplacean ideal. We cannot obtain the kind of exact information necessary for Laplace's prediction of future events. If we could, the hunter would never miss.

The effect of observation—the fact that the observer becomes a part of the system he is examining—is at least a part of the significance of Heisenberg's uncertainty principle, which Eddington unfortunately named the "principle of indeterminacy." This principle does not mean, as Eddington's label apparently suggests, that the world itself is indeterminate in the sense of having a built-in chaos which can then be the occasion for God's manipulation or interference,[3] but instead, that our knowledge has a built-in limitation which becomes more and more apparent as we deal with events on a smaller scale. At the level of gross sensory events, interference resulting from observation is imperceptible. The photons which enable us to see the billiard ball do not perceptibly compete with the cue in our hands in affecting its motion; hence we assume that our visual observation leaves it unaffected. The situation might be different, however, if the only way to observe it was to hit it with the cue.

We have always been aware of the effect of our ob-

[3] Cf. William G. Pollard, *Chance and Providence: God's Action in a World Governed by Scientific Laws* (New York: Charles Scribner's Sons, 1958).

servations and perceptions in our dealing with other human individuals, which is one of the reasons why we have believed that human beings are of a fundamentally different kind from billiard balls. In drawing this conclusion, we have mistakenly identified the individuals involved. A billiard ball is not an individual. It is a vast population of individuals of electron size, whose behavior as a mass in the billiard ball is dealt with in statistical terms as a probability statement. Since in this population, individual effect and variation smooth out to give a great regularity and uniformity of mass behavior, many statements about the population, the ball, can be assigned a very high probability, approaching certainty for practical purposes. When human individuals are massed in the same way, the same regularity, uniformity, and high probability appear.

When we turn to the actual individuals themselves, human or electron, all we can predict is the probability that the given individual will fall as a given point in the total range of possibilities in the mass. We can say nothing precisely about the individual as an individual. For example, although we can state with great precision what the half-life of a radioactive substance is, we have no way of knowing when or whether a given atom will decay. The same consideration applies to life insurance mortality tables and to the individual purchasers of policies.

In scientific practice today, statistical methods are used to reduce the variation of individual behavior to mass units of being which are connected in fixed ways, so that changes at one point can be precisely coordinated with specific and predictable changes at other points in the system. Scientific knowledge, while statistical in form, still gives us a determined world, a world composed of these more or less arbitrarily bounded population units, where events can be anticipated with high probability because we have set them into this kind of pattern of defined relationships. We cannot conclude from this picture that the world *is* of this precisely determinate character. That question we simply cannot answer either way, and it is not legitimate to pretend that we can. What we have done is to decide to describe the world in the terms of science, and what we mean by scientific knowledge is an account of events which shows them to be determined by the component factors we have identified.

Determinism is not a conclusion about the nature of the world, but a methodological principle. Many events in the world appear to submit readily and fully to this kind of highly deterministic analysis—for example, large populations of human beings and events which give no perceptible evidence that they are aware of our own presence, like the "physical" processes of chemical change. It is, therefore, not a long step to the conclusion that the world itself is deterministic in kind, or at least that the world of scientific investigation is that kind of world.

This conclusion, however, fails to take into account the fact that scientific knowledge is a human construction according to specific standards of demonstration. The day is past when most scientists assumed that this knowledge construction actually recovered the inherent nature and structure of the world itself. But this assumption is still being perpetuated by those who turn an invaluable methodological principle into a demonstrated conclusion about the world by saying that because we can and do describe the world deterministically, it is in fact a wholly determined order of events. The more sophisticated among us are more modest about our ability to penetrate the inner secrets of the natural world. We believe that the world does have a structure, else it would not be so patient of our deterministic pattern of interpretations. "But," as Charles Williams has remarked, "patterns are baleful things, and more so because the irony of the universe has ensured that any pattern invented by man shall find an infinite number of facts to support it."[4] The world is also patient of other patterns than determinism, and our exercise of our freedom in developing these patterns confronts us with a paradox when we turn our deterministic interpretation upon our own freedom.

THE PATTERN OF PROOF

WHILE science is something people do, they do it according to criteria which have been defined to be independent of persons. Proof in science is possible precisely because "being scientific" means to abide by the results given by those independent criteria. Many people have assumed that the essential criterion consists in exhibiting some specific sensory event. In ordinary experience this is the way we seem to do it. A line in the X-ray picture means a broken bone; and it is not necessary to eat an egg to determine that it has gone bad. The world is presumed to have a self-evident character disclosed in direct sensory reports, and these sense data constitute the "facts" about the world.

Actually, seeing is not believing. If it were, divergent reports of auto accidents would be impossible, and the fact that on occasion the water witch finds water would prove that dowsing really works. However, the

[4] Charles Williams, "Autocriticisms—9," *Week-End Review,* Vol. VIII, No. 193 (November 18, 1933), p. 525.

skeptical fail to be convinced by a successful performance, while the dowser's occasional failure does not discourage those who believe that water witching does work.[5] Proof requires more than a sensory datum. Proof depends upon interpreting the sensory event to show how it is related to the rest of what we know about the world. Since science deals with our understanding of a world which we perceive through our senses, interpretation and event cannot be severed. The event occurs; science is concerned with how we shall understand the event; and this understanding constitutes the formal structure of scientific reasoning. This is the structure of theory woven around the concrete events of experience to display their relationships and interconnections, thus clothing them with significance and evidential weight. The given event which is adduced as evidence finally becomes evidence because the theory defines for it a specific connection with other events.

Scientific reasoning is hypothetical or theoretical, but these terms are used in a formal and precise sense, not in the way they are popularly used. "That is only a theory," or "Good in theory but not in practice," or "That is only a hypothetical case," are familiar ways of indicating that an idea is only an idle fancy and has no relation to the "real" world of concrete events. Scientific theory is not in this sense speculative, and no theoretical construction can be called scientific if it is divorced from actual events.

The distinction between theory and hypothesis is more in scope of phenomena embraced than in any difference of function. In practice, a hypothesis is usually considered to be a fairly narrow and precise statement

[5] Cf. Evon Z. Vogt and Ray Hyman, *Water Witching U.S.A.* (Chicago: University of Chicago Press, 1959).

applying to a carefully restricted situation that has been arranged for experimental test, while a theory embraces a much larger range of phenomena into a single pattern and may involve a number of hypotheses. We speak, for example, of the theory of evolution—although many biologists now maintain that it is a settled principle and no longer open to question—rather than to the hypothesis of evolution. In either case the logical function is the same, and a sharp distinction between them is mere pedantry.

Formally, the term hypothetical or theoretical means two things at once. One is that the stated pattern of explanation is a proposal to be tested: it is a tentative explanation or pattern of connection that is to be used as the basis for experimentation. It is not being put forward as a settled conclusion about the nature of things. Second, the term hypothesis defines the form of the test, and schematically the form can be represented by the very elementary "If . . . then . . ." form of statement.

What the hypothetical form of statement asserts is a connection between the antecedent (the "if . . ." portion of the statement) and the consequent (the "then . . ." portion) which enables one to make inferences about the truth of one part, given the truth of the other. Exactly what can be validly inferred is governed by the rules of the hypothetical syllogism in elementary logic. In a scientific hypothesis, a particular antecedent-consequent relationship is proposed as a question to be answered by experiment or observation to discover whether these events or factors do combine in the manner defined by the hypothesis.

Without some hypothesis, one would have no clues to direct his attention, or scheme by which to organize the data his random observation produced. If one did begin with random observation—as no scientist would—as soon as he began even to suspect a repetitive sequence, he would then be using a primitive hypothesis to guide his further observations. Specifically, a hypothesis constitutes a precise question, as contrasted to a vague curiosity, and an explicit pattern for experimentation in contrast to mere fumbling or random trial and error. It specifies a possible functional connection among factors, by identifying the item to be looked for and the occurrence or change to be expected. An obvious example is a cause-effect relationship. If it were a short circuit in the lamp that caused the fuse to blow, then another fuse will blow when the lamp is plugged in again—and sure enough, the second fuse does blow. A causes B; A is performed or observed, and B happens. In many situations, the experimenter must deal with B rather than A, because A is beyond his reach or is too vast in scope to deal with directly. The more comprehensive scientific theories can be tested only in this way: first by inferring what consequents would follow if the antecedent theory were true, and then designing experiments or planning observations to determine whether the consequent occurs.

A clear example of the latter procedure appears in the famous Michelson-Morley measurement of the velocity of light in 1881. The question at stake (the antecedent) was whether there was an ether medium through which light waves travelled. If there were such a medium, it should affect the velocity of light (the consequent) just as the current in a river affects the speed of a rowboat depending upon whether the boat is going against or across the current. In their experiment, Michelson and Morley used the rotation of the earth to produce the difference between going against an ether "wind" or across it, by setting their apparatus first parallel with the earth's rotation, and then at right angles to it, the surface speed of the rotating earth being great enough to make a measurable difference in velocities if the ether had any effect. But no difference in velocity could be detected, therefore there must be no "ether" medium for the vibrations of light waves. In this case: If A then B, but since no B could be discovered, A must be ruled out.

If A causes B, then when A occurs, B must also occur. The only alternative is to reject the statement that A causes B. If, given A, B does not occur, then we can conclude that A is not its cause, and the hypothesis is shown to be false. On the other hand, from the occurrence of B, we cannot infer the certainty that A causes B, for the simple reason that some other factor, instead, may be the cause. Automobile accidents can cause death, but it does not follow with certainty that a given death was due to an automobile collision even though the deceased was involved in the accident. He may have suffered a heart attack which precipitated the accident. The hypothetical form of statement and the pattern of reasoning it represents warns us not to assert more exclusive connections between events than we can discover, and also warns us that we can draw some inferences about the relation of antecedent and consequent with certainty but we cannot draw others with an equal certainty.

So far, I have sketched scientific reasoning as a deductive pattern, rather than as the inductive process science is popularly supposed to be. Many people have distinguished science from religion on just this point by saying that scientific reasoning is inductive, while religion and theology are deductive. This formula misrepresents both activities and both processes of reasoning. Religion and theology begin with experience exactly as science does, and not with a set of *a priori* principles from which experience is to be deduced.

Present-day scientists are aware of the large part deduction plays in scientific thinking, and the prominence of mathematics is the clearest sign of this. The distinction between induction and deduction is not a distinction between two different methods of reasoning, and the popular definitions of both are inadequate. Deduction is *not* correctly defined as moving from general propositions or principles to specific conclusions, as seems to be the case in the traditional syllogism: All men are mortal; Socrates is a man; therefore Socrates is mortal. Induction is *not* correctly defined as making or establishing generalizations on the basis of a collection of specific instances, or as moving from a part to the whole. These popular definitions presume that the two processes are fundamentally different kinds of reasoning with different logical structures, and this is a mistake.

The precise distinction is that deduction produces conclusions that are certain, while induction produces conclusions that are at best probable. The difference in the security of the conclusions lies in the *direction* inference moves through the same logical structure, not in the fact that two quite different processes are being employed. In deduction, one infers a conclusion from the premises, or a consequent from the given antecedent, and this can be done with certainty because the premises specify the conditions and limits within which one is to work. In induction one infers premises for a conclusion already given, or an antecedent for a given consequent, and this cannot be done with certainty, because one can never be sure that he has exhausted all the possible antecedents or relevant premises.

Most scientific work today makes use of mathematics as its deductive tool. By reducing the factors in the situation to numbers or symbols, possible consequents can be computed in situations as complex as the effect of gravitational attraction upon a beam of light, or the state of the weather, or the conduct of wars, or the effects of economic policies, or the design of transmission systems for electric power. Mathematics is the most powerful and versatile tool so far invented for exploring possible patterns of interaction, and is so extensively used that the notion has become rife that unless a phenomenon is treated mathematically, it is not being handled scientifically. But science and mathematics are not synonymous.

The other movement of scientific reasoning has been called induction, but would more accurately be called retroduction, a term suggested long ago by C. S. Peirce. Retroduction is the process of inferring possible antecedents for the observed occurrences, in answer to the question, "What must have been the case in order for these observed events to have occurred?" Formally, it is the process of inferring a hypothesis for which the given phenomena are the consequent.[6] Every physician uses it when he confronts the problem of identifying the disease from the reported symptoms, and every detective-story reader is familiar with its ramifications. Failure to recognize the logical identity between formal deduction and retroduction has led to the facile, but unilluminating, schema of the scientific method as consisting of collecting data and then of framing hypotheses by some sort of generalizing process.

[6] Cf. N. R. Hanson, *Patterns of Discovery* (Cambridge: The University Press, 1958), Chapter IV.

In actual practice, scientific reasoning constantly shifts back and forth in these two directions. What we already know about the world provides the basis for deductions about the course of events. These expectations are upset by an unforeseen event, or a problem arises because an anomaly appears. We apply whatever we know about the situation to derive a plausible hypothesis by retroduction, perhaps in the form of a course of action to set the situation right again. This latter stage has been given less than adequate attention because of the widespread belief that the discovery or invention of hypotheses was either a psychological problem or an impenetrable secret of genius. Imagination is certainly called for in inventing hypotheses and in choosing from among them, but the logical structure of the process is not mysterious, and the test of correctness is clear.

The test for an adequate hypothesis is: "Can the given event or situation be deduced from this proposal?" Many possible explanations or hypotheses immediately go down the drain if one already knows anything about the area of the phenomenon. This is why laymen seldom make significant scientific discoveries; they simply do not know enough about the specific field to invent promising hypotheses. If the hypothesis generated by retroduction does seem promising, formal deduction is called into play as the investigator deduces possible consequents as implications of the proposal, to serve as guides for his experimental work to test the hypothesis.

This logical pattern of deductive and retroductive movement between antecedent conditions and consequent events is beautifully illustrated in the classical case of Leverrier's prediction (1846) of the existence and location of Neptune. It had long been known that the orbit of Uranus exhibited irregularities, and Leverrier, applying the clue of Newton's principle of gravitational attraction, reasoned that they could be explained only by the gravitational effect of another and hitherto unknown planet outside the orbit of Uranus. From the data of the observed path of Uranus, Leverrier calculated the orbit and position of the required planet, and sent these data to Galle, a German astronomer, who shortly afterward announced the discovery of a new planet, Neptune, at the place in the sky where Leverrier had told him to look for it.

Leverrier clearly was reasoning from effect to cause to answer the question, "Why these irregularities in the orbit of Uranus?" That Neptune was found where he said it would be has been hailed as the crowning feat of classical Newtonian mechanics. Interestingly, the planet had been observed prior to Galle's announcement, but it had not been identified as a new object in the sky because its observer did not realize that he should be looking for a new heavenly body. The fact that Neptune had already been observed, but not identified, demonstrates that confirmation consists of more than actually locating an object in the sky. It must be an object with a particular meaning, such as that specified in the hypothesis spelled out in Leverrier's calculations.

Leverrier's further career is equally instructive, because after his triumph with Uranus, he turned his attention to a similar problem concerning the orbit of Mercury, for which he proposed a similar explanation, namely that Mercury's perturbations must be caused by a planet inside Mercury's orbit, which he named Vulcan. Accordingly, he computed Vulcan's orbit and described the characteristics Vulcan must have to cause the observed irregularities in Mercury's orbit. But Vulcan has never been observed, and now nobody is looking for it because relativity theory provides a different and more adequate explanation for the behavior of Mercury. Leverrier's failure to find Vulcan was fatal to this theory and contributed to the revision of classical mechanics. As Hanson has said, "It cannot have been the fate of many physicists to have served both as the saviour and as the executioner of a physical theory."[7]

The proof lies in reasoning, not in the raw datum that Neptune can be seen in a telescope, or that Vulcan has not been seen. By reasoning, a total system of internally consistent statements is established which also describes and identifies specific events in the world of experience. Both these requirements must be held together, for it was the second which failed in the case of Vulcan. A consistent set of statements—calculations—is easy to achieve if they need not refer to observed events. Similarly, it is easy to describe what is going on if one does not need to make sense out of the flow of events by setting them into a pattern of meaningful relationships with the rest of experience. Scientific demonstration consists in bringing both these together by formulating the pattern of statements, ideally stated as laws, which give order to concrete events, and that formulation is most nearly true which gives order to the largest range of experiences.

A further consideration is the fact that no concrete sequence of events exists in isolation from the rest of the total flow of events, and, frequently, considerable expenditure of technical ingenuity is required to isolate the experimental situation sufficiently to examine it. This interconnection appears formally also. It is very rare that a given hypothesis has only a single consequent, and almost equally rare that a given consequent

[7] *Ibid.*, p. 204.

can be derived from only one antecedent. Moreover, the antecedent itself is a consequent of other antecedents, and the consequent becomes in turn an antecedent from which other consequent events can be inferred. The result is not that we have a collection of parallel and disconnected lines of inference, but instead a web of interconnecting strands of inference, so that almost never does a specific deductive-retroductive inference stand alone. This interconnection of lines of inference has been called convergence of evidence. Evidence converges as a given situation involves an enlarging fabric of interrelated antecedents and consequents. As new experiences enter the picture, and as our understanding of the processes involved changes, the pattern of explanation will also change to take account of the wider range of data and these new understandings.

When the plain man asks for the "facts," therefore, he is asking for something which is far more subtle and complex and far less stable than he thinks. He means by "facts" the firmly fixed and final conclusions of science—when he does not mean those equally firmly fixed data of experience which can have only one unambiguous meaning. What he wants are the "facts" freed from speculation, hedging, and finespun distinctions, in other words, freed from their theoretical costume, as if they existed in complete independence from all other events and meanings. But facts are striptease artists; as the last bit of costume drops away they fade from view. "Facts," as firmly fixed and final things, do not exist. The fact is not the sensory signal or the datum from the outside world standing all by itself, but the meaning the datum carries. The fact is what the datum *means,* and that meaning is derived from the costume of theory draped about the datum in order to understand it by setting it into relationship with the rest of our experience. Data do not carry their own interpretation built in, as any layman discovers when he struggles vainly to penetrate the scientist's explanation of his graphs or pointer readings. What a datum means depends upon how theory fits it into a total context of interpretation. Thus an event, an observation, an object, is not itself a fact. It becomes a fact when it is interpreted in terms of some theoretical pattern, and the factual content changes as the theoretical pattern changes. In other words, evidence does not always converge upon the same conclusion about the nature of the event and its relation to the rest of the world. The choice between alternative patterns of understanding depends finally upon the decision as to which way of understanding the data makes the most coherent sense out of our total knowledge of the world.

A dramatic example of a shift in the meaning of concrete data, of a shift in convergence of evidence, of "facts," is provided by the checkered career of Piltdown Man, *Eoanthropus dawsoni,* who astounded the scientific world in 1912 as a native English fossil progenitor of modern man, and who, in the early 1950's was retired in disgrace as a fraud upon science.[8] The Piltdown artifacts were first presented to the scientific world by their finders, Woodward and Dawson, as an early form of man found on English soil. The fragments consisted of a human cranium and an apelike jaw bone with two teeth still attached, associated bones of extinct animals and some crude stone tools, a canine tooth found the following year by Teilhard de Chardin, and further remains

[8] A full account of the affair is given by one of the scientists who participated in unmasking the fraud in Joseph S. Weiner, *The Piltdown Forgery* (London: Oxford University Press, 1955).

from another site found in 1915. According to the evolutionary theory of the time, man developed his enlarged brain before he lost his apelike lower face, and these remains exhibited that pattern. Geological evidence confirmed a great age for the fossils, and Piltdown Man was entered on the family tree of man.

It is important to note that the paleontologists pruned Piltdown Man from man's genealogy by using the same line of reasoning which had grafted him on in the first place. While the remains fitted the evolutionary pattern as it had then been worked out, during succeeding decades many other human fossil remains were found, and the best interpretation of these pointed toward a different sequence of development, namely, that man's lower face, his jaw and teeth, developed very early, while his enlarged brain was among the last features to appear. Thus paleontolgy was confronted with remains indicating two divergent lines of development for modern man, with Piltdown representing a most conspicuous exception to the pattern exhibited by all other human fossils. Whatever was to be done with the evidence, the conceptual problem was the same: to arrange the fossils in a meaningful sequence in terms of the assumption of evolutionary relationship. Because of Piltdown's anomalous character in comparison to the other fossils, there was an increasing tendency during the years to ignore him in describing man's evolution, but the remains existed and had to be taken into account.

In 1953 the Piltdown remains were intensively studied by a number of recently developed techniques, and a mass of new data was exposed. Chemical tests on the bones disclosed that the cranium and jawbone were of quite different compositions. When the bones were drilled for samples, the jawbone acted like fresh bone, while the cranium acted like fossil bone. When the teeth were carefully examined, the form of wear seemed artificial and scratches similar to file marks were discovered on the worn surfaces, and a tiny fragment of iron alloy was found embedded in the surface of the detached canine tooth. Moreover, experiments with an iron file on a chimpanzee molar produced patterns of wear that were essentially identical to those of the Piltdown teeth.

The logical question was: What hypothetical antecedent would best explain this body of phenomena as consequent? That is, from what situation could these phenomena be best deduced? The most plausible general hypothesis was that all these tests taken together indicated that the cranium and jaw did not belong to the same creature, so that Piltdown was at best two creatures, not one, and that the scratches on the teeth indicated manufacture, and this in turn indicated that the combination of jaw and cranium was deliberately arranged. It would not be impossible for the bones of a single creature to exhibit differing chemical and physical states, but no one would hold this explanation to be as likely as that which postulated two creatures of different ages. Similarly, the fact that one could imitate the natural wear on a tooth by using a file on it would not prove that the original was also an artifact. However, an equally weighty piece of evidence was the fact that Piltdown could not be fitted into the evolutionary sequence leading to modern man. Therefore, everything would be simpler, particularly evolutionary theory as a whole, if *Eoanthropus dawsoni* were regarded as a deliberate construction, salted in the gravels of the River Ouse at Piltdown.

The decisive criterion operating at the conclusion of the story is the same as that which functioned at its beginning: a consistent set of statements interpreting a specific set of data from the empirical world is to be correlated with other sets of statements interpreting other empirical data, so that the whole world of experience is shown to be as nearly of one piece as we can achieve. The judgment on Piltdown Man which best fits now with what we know about the world is that the remains were deliberately manufactured, and that the job was very convincingly done to fit the pattern that was being propounded by the evolutionary theorists of the time. Successively, the one set of remains has carried four different meanings or factual contents: (1) that Piltdown Man is an ancestor of man because man's human brain developed earlier than his human jaw and face; (2) that here is a fortuitous combination of remains from two creatures, one human and the other ape, as some scientists had held from the beginning; (3) that they represent divergent evolutionary developments, with Piltdown exhibiting a unique sequence of events; (4) that what we have here is fraud. At no stage in the shifts of interpretation did the sheer existence of the bones constitute proof of anything. As bones, they were simply events demanding to be fitted into some total understanding of how the world operates, and specifically of how man became the creature he now is.

Whether one is working in science or in theology, he can properly maintain that there is such a thing as error, not to mention fraud, and that it can be identified, along with an approximation of the truth. He must also acknowledge that not everyone will accept or support his demonstration of error or of truth, because not all persons seek or recognize the same total pattern of meaning in the experienced world.

Finally, scientific proof consists of an explanation which successfully explains. "An event is explained when it is traced to other events which require less explanation; when it is shown to be part of an intelligible pattern of events."[9] The crux lies in the definition of "successful," because there is a vast difference between exhibiting that intelligible pattern and persuading someone who rejects it that he has been refuted. Too often, the claim that proof is possible in science, but not in religion, has been taken to mean that the demonstration of an error (or truth) in scientific terms, automatically dismisses all objections to it, and wins instant agreement from everybody. The history of science is replete with instances of failure here. It may be true that the ideal scientist spends his major efforts in refuting his own cherished theories, as Darwin said he himself did, but the "Letters" section of *Science*[10] offers continuous testimony that evidence which suffices to persuade some scientists fails to persuade others.

Persuasiveness requires that the operative factors in the pattern of explanation be those we are prepared to accept. If we believe that nothing is real except that which is visible and material, then no explanation in any other terms can persuade us. If we are already committed to the view that the only links between events must be neutral, quantitative, impersonal, measurable energy exchanges, which is the picture we specify for science, then no other explanation can be acceptable to

[9] Hanson, p. 94.

[10] The weekly journal of The American Association for the Advancement of Science.

us. At the last, the process turns full circle to confront us with the requirement that we must clearly recognize the presence of our own expectations and commitments in our observations and conclusions. What we find depends upon the question we have begun with and upon what we will accept as an answer at the end. Nonetheless, science is tied to the empirical world; it is not an unanchored speculative construction, and scientists are properly confident of their results, especially when they can show that they have added a few more strands to our growing web of knowledge of the world.

Part Four ✵

DOING THE TRUTH

Chapter Seven ✵

RELATIVITY WITHOUT RELATIVISM

Is there knowledge? it will vanish away; for our knowledge and our prophecy alike are partial, and the partial vanishes when wholeness comes. When I was a child, my speech, my outlook, and my thoughts were all childish. When I grew up, I had finished with childish things. Now we see only puzzling reflections in a mirror, but then we shall see face to face. My knowledge now is partial; then it will be whole, like God's knowledge of me.

(NEB) I Corinthians 13:9–12

THE DIALECTIC IN KNOWLEDGE

THE enthusiastic attachment to science in our culture expresses the prevalent but mistaken assumption that knowledge is a kind of deposit one possesses, and to which he adds as he receives and retains the information provided by the external world. Knowledge is considered to be a collection and not a creation. While one may be active in designing questions and experimental situations, his contribution to increasing the sum of knowledge is presumed to be essentially that of a passive recorder of the character of the world about him. The roots of this view go deep in our history, and they feed from both the empiricist and rationalist strands in our culture. Whether the form of truth is found in the patterns of reason itself or in the content of sensory experience, knowledge is presumed to have a uniform structure for all persons, so that the same evidence should be equally persuasive for each person.

The content of religion, as well as science, has been expected to exhibit this uniform and universally persuasive character, and the failure of religion to provide this content has not significantly undermined the predominant notion that such knowledge exists. Instead, this failure of religion has shifted the burden of providing it to science, and we live in an age when religion, rather than science, is on the defensive.

The error in this presumption about the nature of knowledge is that it conceals the person's participation in the creation of his knowledge. Furthermore, the massive success of scientific techniques in bringing various aspects of nature under a degree of human control does not eliminate the person from scientific knowledge. It only permits us to forget that he is present as the active agent in creating it.

Knowledge is structured experience; it is the way we participate with something beyond ourselves which we do not create; it is the pattern by which we guide our interaction with whatever confronts us. In our knowledge, we declare the meaning we seek in our interchange with whatever surrounds us, because our knowledge states the way we understand events are related to each other, and this is as true in science as in religion. The splendid elegance of the periodic table of the elements represents as much a pattern for our action with the world as it does an inherent structure in that natural world. In the same way, the words of the Psalmist, "The fear of the Lord is the beginning of wisdom,"[1] or the words given to Jesus in the Fourth Gospel, "thy word is truth,"[2] express both the nature of God and man's response to him.

The clue to knowledge is in the verb, not in the noun. Knowledge is created in interaction, not accumulated. Neither is it a gift we receive through the senses as if all we had to do was look, or something residing as a ready-made pattern in our minds, or a body of truths delivered intact by God to a prophet, or engraved by him or an angel on plates of stone or gold, or written in the original autographs of the biblical books.

Knowledge created in interaction means that there are two poles in the knowing process. In order to know, person and world or person and God must meet, and their meeting begets an ineradicable dialectical tension within the knowledge which is asserted to result from the meeting. Knowing does not consist in successfully possessing the essence of something; knowing is interacting, because all knowledge, including knowledge of ourselves, can be gained only within a matrix of relationships. To know requires that we enter into some kind of relationship which will provide a pattern for understanding and action. Both we and the world participate in creating that relationship in which we live and through which we know. We have long been aware of the role the world plays in our knowing, but we have been less aware that we are part of our knowledge because we must act from within the relationship in which we gain our knowledge. Because knowledge

[1] Psalm 111:10.
[2] John 17:17.

stands within this relationship we cannot so separate ourselves from whatever meets us that we can identify its nature as it is in itself. Neither can we so separate ourselves from the world around us that we can know ourselves freed from the pressures of whatever surrounds us. Our knowledge of God is in no better situation. He cannot so reveal himself that we are protected from misunderstanding him unless he denies our status as persons by overwhelming us.

Because we know and act from within relationship, nothing in our knowledge so captures or guarantees the character of whatever confronts us that we can act with complete impunity and safety within the security of certain knowledge. Our actual situation is that we are compelled to act in some fashion, if only to seek refuge from whatever confronts us. But we *do* confront something—or more concretely, something confronts us. In part because of the mystery of its nature, it demands that we respond, and until we have responded we cannot know what its nature is.

By asking "What confronts us?" we acknowledge that we are not selves or persons in a vacuum, but live in relation to something other than ourselves and act in response to it. That Something imposes restrictions and sets boundaries and lays conditions, whether we take the initiative toward it or respond to its initiative. (This is one of the facets of meaning in the claim that God is creator and the ground of being.) Were no resistance offered, we could not act at all. A world which did not resist us could not support us; it would be a world in which no action would be possible, for it would have no relationship within which action could occur. Sometimes we entertain the fantasy of a frictionless world—until our car skids on the ice—or a world without gravitation—until we realize the problems of the astronauts with weightlessness. When we talk of the influence of the environment upon our own or any person's decisions, we are pointing to those conditions within which we live and act, and which provide us with the stability and security that, even physically, we cannot live without.

We are compelled to be selves in relationship even before the conditions within which we must act have been clearly stated. If those conditions could be clearly and completely stated, we would be relieved of the necessity for being the responsible selves we have to be. The dialectic of our situation is that without relationship beyond itself, the self as person would be nothing at all, but equally, the self as person would be nothing if it were no more than the focus of these relationships, a point through which forces flow.

All knowing is the act of faith by which the person meets his world, and reflects the quest of faith in which one does not start with a fixed external world or a final and absolute truth to guide his action for him. He must brave the mystery armed only with what he already knows without assurance that it is correct or final or sufficient. He faces risks of error and failure, and to accept these risks by responding is the venture of faith by which knowledge is increased.

We know the agony in this act of faith when we cannot accept what our fellows affirm, and they reject our insights as false. When we refuse their evidence as illusory, and the evidence which demonstrates for us fails to persuade them, we begin to realize that knowledge is a pattern of understanding we create and within which we act, and that truth is a proclamation of the self in faith. How can we prove that the meaning which orders our own world of experience is true and should be true for all? The attempt to prove and to persuade becomes the dialogue of persons in which we build the community of response and shared understanding wherein each one finds his measure of resistance, freedom, and support.

In this living community of shared understanding, we see again the double, dialectical character of knowledge, that it has both a universal, impartial, communal dimension and a concrete, personal dimension. Knowledge must represent more than private sentiments or solitary perceptions or individual insights, because these cannot be shared or set against impartial standards, and cannot show how one person's experience and insight are related to another's. Neither can knowledge be wholly neutral and external, validated solely by impartial and universal standards, because it must satisfy the person's own expectations and fulfill his own vision of his integrity as a person. Within its texture, he must be able to see himself as the kind of person he wills to be. Between these two poles knowledge lives and grows. The tension cannot be dissolved, and it is in this tension that science and religion stand.

BOUNDARY CONDITIONS

THE relationship between science and religion cannot be reduced to the simple decision to accept one or the other as true. While both are rooted in the same flow of experience, they order its events in terms of different meanings, and therefore they depict two different worlds. One consists of a self-contained world of nature, including man, which is described as a series of physical-chemical events that are identified as measurable changes occurring in space and time. In this world, the clue to specific events lies in the larger principles or laws which they exhibit, and outside the processes of nature there are no forces or purposes that give it direction. The other world includes both man and nature in a domain of personal action and response. Here the clue to events is to be found in the nature of persons, and the clue to meaning is God's action to redeem a broken world and to restore it to himself.

In each of these different worlds, the events of natural and human history and our individual lives can be ordered and made coherent. So stated, the two patterns of meaning are distinctly separated from each other, and each is complete within itself. Neither picture can be taken as providing only a partial knowledge which the other view fills out and supports, and they are not complementary in the sense that each deals with certain phenomena inappropriate to the other, as in the dual wave and particle character of light, so that both would be required for a complete account of experience. They cannot be superimposed, one upon the other, as if one were the floor plan and the other the front elevation of the same house.[3] So far the question would seem to be that of choosing between them, affirming one and rejecting the other, and by making this choice we pretend that we have escaped the dialectic of our situation. But, notwithstanding the enthusiasm of our culture for science, neither its methods nor those of religion offers any release from the risks of error and failure inherent in our limited and contingent situation. Neither way of viewing the world or experience can stand as a final and certain body of knowledge, because both express

[3] Cf. C. A. Coulson, *Science and Christian Belief* (Chapel Hill: The University of North Carolina Press, 1955), Chapter 3.

the relativity and finitude of our existence. Neither way of understanding ourselves and the world can be permitted to absorb and obliterate the other without denying the ineradicable dialectic in our knowing. One cannot be abandoned and the other affirmed without denying the biblical claim that God acts and man responds in the same realm of human and natural history which science studies.

The intention of the original questions with which each begins makes their dialectical relation clear. Science, by beginning with "What?" describes an object presented for analysis in neutral and universal terms. To this end one can make himself, as well as other things and other human beings, an object for such analysis, for the goal is to describe as accurately as possible what the conditions of one's existence are. Religion, by beginning from "Who am I?" is concerned with the subject himself, not by way of analysis as if he were an object to be scrutinized, but as the active agent who declares himself, proclaims the meaning he seeks, and thus establishes his being, for this exercise of freedom and initiative is the sole answer to the primordial religious question.

Clearly, the intention in both questions produces abstractions in the strict sense. Each represents an ideal case: the pure self at one extreme, and at the other extreme, the world, or the things in it, as a wholly impersonal system of forces and impacts. At one extreme, everything is to be explained or understood in terms of the inner life, initiative, and freedom of the self who acts. At the other extreme, everything is to be understood in terms of the intersection of the forces and bodies constituting the event. At one extreme nothing is predictable, because the freedom of the self is the keynote. At the other, everything is predictable, because all events are wholly determined by, and are fully explained in terms of, their known constituent factors.

These two questions and their answers stand to each other as logical limits or boundary conditions upon each other. Selves do not exist in a pure scientific world, while in a world of pure selves, science is not possible. The dialectic between these boundaries, or limiting categories, cannot be dissolved because we live between their confines. We recognize this fact in our experience whenever we attempt to analyze our own behavior and motivations by asking, "Why did we do that?" The answer we want is one which shows how our apparently free action followed from the play of external circumstances and pressures upon us, not to mention whatever interior motivations or drives that can be identified. While often enough we use this approach to shift the blame from ourselves by trying to show that we could not help ourselves, we really want to know how we are bound into the web of events around us. We want to explain ourselves to ourselves in terms of the conditions surrounding us, because only thus can we understand ourselves within the world of events. But if we could succeed in fully explaining ourselves as the product of the forces acting upon us, we would cease to be free and responsible persons, for the kind of explanation we try to achieve would deny that we are persons at all. Yet without denying that external factors do influence us and limit us, we remember that the personal mystery within ourselves initiated the inquiry in the first place.

The same dialectic of boundary conditions appears in many forms. This is the tension between freedom and determinism. However freedom as a fact of experience is defined, it has some flavor of contradiction to determinism. To call freedom self-determinism, as many people wish to do, confirms the plain man's suspicion that the freedom we are talking about does not really exist at all. In the strict sense, both concepts are abstractions because they identify limiting conditions. A completely determined world would not allow sufficient freedom to discover the fact of determinism, while in a completely free world there would be no contact or relationship at all.

The tension between justice and love exhibits another form of this dialectic. Even though Christians insist that both terms are true of God, the conflict between them remains in our experience, and we consider it a chilly love, indeed, which always operates within the confines of evenhanded justice. St. Paul's contrast between the Law and the Gospel provides another example. Law, unrelieved by the Gospel, generates moralistic self-righteousness when it does not become a Procrustean bed, while Gospel without the Law melts into feverish sentimentality. So, while St. Paul rejected the Law as the path of salvation, he had no hesitation in issuing moral commands to Christians who had failed to perform as Christians should.

The recurring debate over the relation between the Jesus of history and the Christ of faith exhibits exactly the same tension within contemporary Christian theology. If the Jesus of history cannot be identified within the narratives which proclaim the Christ of the Easter faith, then that Christ becomes a mythological figure with no anchor in history, and therefore a purely private and interior kind of notion. From the other direction, if the facts about the career of Jesus in Galilee and Judea and the actual words he spoke are the sole basis for our faith, then there is no faith but only historical research.

The traditional problem of miracles stands within the same dialectic of understanding. The world we describe in terms of the fixed connections of natural law has no place for the action of God, while a world of miracles would have no pattern by which we could understand it. The issue is not whether God can act to suspend or to interfere with an otherwise orderly pattern of nature. The issue is how we are to understand what does happen. Although we are more modest about the finality of natural law than an earlier generation was, we still attempt to reduce all events, even unexpected ones which might be called miracles, to regular and fixed patterns, so that God's action tends to disappear. We still employ the category of miracle to assert that God's will and action are the clue to meaning in a world we have so defined that God cannot act unless he breaks the laws of nature. We have not yet achieved the biblical view in which all events communicate his presence and participation. We talk of miracles because we cannot see God and nature together, as if we can see God in nature only by his interference with it.

These limits represent directions in which we look and criteria by which we judge while we are standing within the flow of events. If we look always in one direction, we discover the world and lose ourselves. If we look always in the other direction the world disappears and our selves occupy the entire stage. Thus, when we interpret our experienced world we cannot evade the ambiguity of our actual situation. Our religious response must be made within a world of concrete things and events. These conditions force their nature so irresistibly upon us that we are tempted to conclude that they determine for us the full texture and extent of our response, and, forgetting our own initiative in responding, we seek to guarantee our response by certifying the historical certainty of the crucial events of biblical religion on grounds the nonbeliever would accept, in the same way that we try to take refuge in the finality of science. Or else in sheer proclamation of our beliefs, we abandon claims for knowledge in religion and reject the necessity for any historical verification or agreement from our fellows. Either way we try to sever the dialectic within which we live and must act.

In their pure or abstract form, religion and science stand as symbols of the two poles in this confrontation between self and world, representing the two foci of interaction within which we create our understanding of our situation. They pull from opposite directions on the same rope, rather than provide different but mutually supporting strands in our fabric of knowledge. What one emphasizes or seeks or discloses the other denies. Yet, if the tension breaks because one end is dropped like one end of the rope in a tug of war, knowledge collapses because interaction between self and world is denied. We then have constructed a world with ourselves missing, or we will have set ourselves at the center of the universe by denying the authenticity of the world around us.

NATURE AND GRACE

THERE is a deeper problem here. So far, we have described a dialectical relation between science and religion as ideal forms in the sense that a scientific law states the ideal or limiting case. However, the relation between science and biblical religion is not so easily resolved. The issue is subtler than the polarity indicated merely by setting them as limits or boundaries upon each other, although this is a great advance over sundering them from each other so that one or the other may be abandoned. The dialectic in knowledge does not run only between science and biblical religion, as if they represented opposite poles. It also runs through each one, and they differ significantly in the way each copes with that dialectic within itself. Or, to put the point in more human terms, science and biblical religion constitute significantly different ways by which man copes with the dialectic in his own existence.

We inescapably need knowledge of the scientific kind about objects in the world around us. Lacking it, we act in ignorance of the ways of the world we face, and while no amount of information in itself will decide for us the question of how we shall participate in the world, it can make us aware of what the consequences of alternative courses of action will probably be. When we act ignorantly, we run the risk of shattering ourselves upon the world's apparently inflexible and insensitive nature: for example, if we fail to take account of the friction differential between the concrete and the spot of ice, down we go, or the car goes off the road. Or, from the other direction, we will attempt to bludgeon the world into compliance with our wills as if we were master to a servant world, rather than living in interchange with it. If we choose in ignorance of what the consequences will be, we may not survive long enough to correct our mistakes. But no degree or kind of knowledge can relieve us of the responsibility to choose the manner of our action, and we must choose before we can know what all the consequences will be. Therefore, it does not follow that we ought necessarily to choose the course of action which most probably will guarantee our survival. Jesus and the Christian martyrs of every age did not do so.

Science is one of the means we have devised to reduce, if we cannot dissolve, the tension in our existence. By science we hope to attain that kind of knowledge of the web of relationships in which we are involved which is sufficiently freed of our participation in its making that it will determine for us the way we should act. Science is human enough, but the goal it serves is the elimination of that human dimension by absorbing the person into the impersonal structure of the world as another instance of its laws and processes. And we extend this intention by holding that the failure to see oneself in these impersonal scientific terms and to act accordingly is ignorance, an ignorance which can be corrected and eliminated by more knowledge of the same kind. The resolution of the dialectic we seek through science, and the resolution many people today assume science provides, is the obliteration of the source of the dialectic, namely ourselves. Although we now know that the human side of science makes that goal impossible for us to attain, the ideal still is to describe a world in which personal responsiveness and responsibility are absent. Insofar as these influence how we describe the way the world operates, our description has fallen short of the objective of science.

Biblical religion, by contrast, not only affirms the dialectic in our living and in our knowing, the authenticity of biblical religion demands that dialectic. Biblical religion is not simply a fact or collection of facts about the world or certain entities in it or which are supposed to be acting upon it. Biblical religion is a relationship offered and accepted; it is a relationship which culminates in the healing of the pain and the redemption of the tragedy of our existence. By asserting with equal force both the act of God and the response from man, biblical religion stands firmly against two opposite tendencies. One is the tendency to interpret religion, and biblical religion specifically, as something wholly interior and private, as something going on wholly inside those particular individuals who happen to have this kind of interest. The other tendency is so completely to externalize and objectify the content and the events of biblical religion that it becomes something wholly given from above, something which man simply receives intact from God. Either way, both the tension in our existence and the authenticity of biblical religion are denied.

Biblical religion cannot be reduced to something internal or solitary that exists only in the thoughts of the believers, because God's acts to disclose himself in Christ, and his work to build his Kingdom, are declared to be as authentically present and as much a part of the concrete world of events as a tornado. And if Biblical religion is to be taken seriously, it is as terrifying in its consequences. But the primary question about these events is not simply whether they can be authenticated as actual events in our common world of experience. The Kingdom of God and the disclosure of God in Christ are not simply events to be described and analyzed, or merely more factors to be added to round out a total description of what is going on. These events confront the person with himself, because they press upon him the question of how he shall respond to the One who confronts him through these events and in them offers a relationship with himself. They press upon the person the question whether the Kingdom is for him, whether he is the sinner for whom Christ died, whether he is the one who needs and can receive the reconciliation offered. The proclamation of this reconciliation in word or deed does not remove the agony of decision, for as one wills to respond or to withdraw he discovers that he decides the meaning of his own existence by the way he chooses to respond. Moreover, he must take this decision without knowing fully what the Kingdom is, or why its price is the cross, or what changes in himself it will demand. And the decision, whichever way it goes, cannot dissolve all doubts or resolve all uncertainties about whether one has correctly read the signs of God's presence and activity.

This demand for a decision either to accept or reject the relationship offered is the reason biblical religion offers no knowledge content of its own to replace the necessary knowledge of the world we gain by scientific methodology. If the content of biblical religion could replace or correct the content of science, then information in and of itself would answer the decision question for us. Biblical religion cannot become an alternative kind of science, and its narrative cannot replace scientific historiography without denying that we participate in the creation of our knowledge. The event—the world—is there to be verified in its own terms; if we deny that, both the creation of the world and God's revelation are denied. But the event must be appropriated, and there is no way to evade the act of appropriation by appealing to the pure event or to the pure revelation itself, for appropriation requires one's participation in, not merely information about, the relationship offered in biblical religion. That is why no historical investigation can establish beyond all doubt or challenge the actuality of any event, and why no event, even when established beyond reasonable doubt, can serve as the guarantor of faith.

Biblical religion promises the healing of the agony of this decision, and the transformation of its tragedy into triumph even in the apparent defeat of the cross. Concretely, the mystery of life remains. We continue to dwell within the ambiguities of existence. But we have in the biblical understanding of the human career both the radical challenge to our pretensions to final and complete knowledge, the denial of the purity and finality of our goals, the rejection of the perfection of our performance, and the promise of healing. In Christ, his life, death, and resurrection, God has condemned the world and ourselves. We also are of the present age which has been found wanting and which therefore must be replaced by the new age to come. From the condition thus described to us, no knowledge of any neutral kind can save us. It is no solution to remind ourselves that we really are no worse than anyone else, and it is still less a solution to submerge ourselves in the vast processes of cosmic change so that we disappear, because as our problem thus is absorbed, so also we drown in the endless flow of events. In the traditional language of the Bible, this is what St. Paul means by the condemning effect of the Law. What we really know about ourselves only makes more clear to us the dialectical condition in which we live because we know that we are of the present age which God has condemned in the cross.

At the same time, in the life, death, and resurrection of Christ, God has acted to disclose the new age that shall be and has made available to us the possibility of participating in its life. Biblical religion does not remove the dialectic in our living and knowing, but it declares its healing by offering the new life of reconciliation in Christ which heals the divisions within us and among us and between ourselves and God. By giving new life in Christ, biblical religion says that God has released among us the power that will heal and transform and redeem our lives. That transforming power has created the community of believers, and Christ continues to live in the midst of this community, knitting their lives together into a community of faith which bridges the centuries from the apostles' day to our own. Thus the biblical doctrine of creation claims the world of nature and of man as the realm of God's activity, and the doctrines of grace and justification proclaim that God acts within this world of nature and man to heal the brokenness, to answer the uncertainty, to transcend the dialectic which cannot be removed.

Whether these things are true cannot be established or verified apart from the dialectical condition of our existence. Biblical religion not only leaves us within the dilemma of judgment, it compels us to acknowledge the dilemma. The answer must be in terms of how one responds to what is offered to him, and what in his own experience he finds to be meaningful and significant. If he finds his own existence made most meaningful by being absorbed into and lost within the great mechanical processes of nature and history, then there will be little persuasiveness and no healing grace in the claim that with the coming of Christ God has acted to give a new direction to history and a new meaning to personal existence. If, by contrast, one finds his own existence integrated and made significant as he responds to the Person in whom God has entered history, then he will find the biblical story true. This choice does not mean that either way of understanding ourselves is a matter of private opinion, that is, that we can make either one true simply by believing it. This choice means instead that we cannot know whether either is true without making a decision for which we are responsible.

Whether one speaks for the truth of a world in which grace is absent, or for the truth that nature is the realm of grace, he speaks from the concreteness of his own existence, and his words exemplify the dialectic in which he lives. However he states the truth he perceives, his words will carry the stamp of his own participation in what he knows and believes.

THE SHAPE OF TRUTH

We have this treasure in earthen vessels.

II CORINTHIANS 4:7

THE BOUNDARIES OF TRUTH

THE CRUCIAL DIFFERENCE between the language of science and the language of biblical religion is to be found in the way each recognizes and preserves the person's participation in his truth. Scientific speech describes a world as neutrally as possible, and from this speech the person has fled. Only a standard unit remains, propelled to and fro by the vast Brownian movement of cosmic forces.

The speech of biblical religion exalts the presence of the person to the point that we are in danger of denying that anything else is there. Here also we describe a world, now not as a neutral thing to be known in the same terms by all, but as that reality to which and in which we respond to God. When we speak biblically about our life as persons we cannot exclude the limitations of our status from our words. Because we cannot find clear and universal formulas which will both express our own response and encompass all time and space, we speak in paradoxes. And because no world or God that can be captured in formal propositions can act to welcome our response, we celebrate our participation by reciting a myth.

Language that is founded upon myth and framed in paradox seems the antithesis of the antiseptic pellucidity which we expect from truth expressed in the logical speech of science. The difference comes because of the direction we are looking. In the one, we look toward the source of our experience and suppress our own response. In the other, we speak from our response and frame our picture of the world in symbols that are developed to carry and sustain our responsive interaction with the world and God. Paradox and myth can be removed from our language, but when they are, words grow cold, phrases limp, and thoughts hang impaled upon the barbs of formal categories.

The choice returns in a new form. What kind of truth do we really want? Those who speak for paradox and myth proclaim the authenticity of the person by whose response the truth is made. Those who deny the propriety of paradox and reject the accuracy of myth speak instead for a neutral world in which all men act alike in lockstep obedience to an impersonal truth which chains them all.

PARADOX

PARADOX results from the recognition that logical rules are guides, not boundaries. If we admitted them as boundaries, we would be saying that outside and above our thought stands a universal pattern of logic to which all our thinking must conform. Those who assert the propriety of paradox do so in order to say that man makes logic; he was not made for it. In using paradox, we acknowledge that experience overflows the rational categories we employ to give symmetry and coherence to our existence. We recognize that we cannot see far enough or clearly enough to discern any single pattern of interpretation which would put every event and relationship into its proper place in the total web of existence.

Paradox is not a license for confusion. Some statements do make others unnecessary or false. Paradox is not a contradiction which can be resolved by choosing one of its halves, or by finding a safe third alternative lying between the extremes. Paradox appears when we have no concepts or categories adequate to embrace all that we must say.

Biblical religion offers many instances of this dilemma: that a man can be at once saint and sinner; that God is both just and loving; that this universe of God's creation not only proceeds with the regularity of law but is also the realm of God's grace and providence; that while man belongs to this world he is not of it because he is a citizen of the heavenly kingdom; and the supreme paradox of all, that God became man in Christ who is at once both fully man and fully God. In all of these examples, we must say more than either half of the statement will carry by itself, just as we must also say that we cannot comprehend our experience if we deny either science or biblical religion.

Paradox is not a virtue; it is a necessity. We cannot take the easier path of ruling out one of the two conflicting statements, because what remains leaves too much of our experience behind and presupposes that we are infinitely less complex than we know we are.

The question is whether we shall erect a paradigm for experience, a logical exemplar for what must be true, and then confine "truth" to what filters through its meshes, or whether the richness, the variety, the tang of life upon the tongue, shall be the master whom our formulas will serve.

If our logic will not permit us to say that Christ is both Very God and Very Man, then so much the worse for logical categories. If, in our ordinary thought, love and justice stand at odds to defeat each other's ends, we still must use them to say what we know of God. Those who eschew anthropomorphism in favor of mechanomorphism, by speaking of God as an impassive force for good which can neither seek justice nor express love, simply fail to say what biblical religion declares man's experience of God to be. By calling the result a paradox, we lay ourselves open to the charge that we have fallen into contradiction because of fuzzy thinking, which is certainly sometimes the case. We cannot deploy paradoxes as mercenaries to forestall our critics from demanding of us that we explain what we mean. But we can enlist the term to defend the position that neither our ordinary understanding of ourselves nor the canons of scientific demonstration nor the patterns of an ideal language shall become barricades beyond which our statements must not venture.

Paradox not only forces us to affirm what we would prefer to extirpate as contradiction; it also lodges heavy blows at our very sense of rationality. Nothing seems more reasonable than to say that if man's problems are to be solved, we must use our intelligence and goodwill to get on with the business of solving them. Nothing seems more rational than to declare that a good man deserves to be saved to a life of future blessedness in reward for his merits, and that God truly loves a righteous man, and that morality is the way to earn his love. Our reasonable natures are offended by the biblical reminder that we cannot save ourselves, that we can only be saved by another, that God's love is given, not earned, and that the price of love is death upon the cross. When St. Paul said that the cross was a stumbling block to Jews and foolishness to Greeks, he was referring to this offense against reason which Christianity proclaims by setting rationality within the life of man and not above it.

It sometimes seems that if we enter here, we will have to abandon reason. Our reasonable natures tell us that unless Christian claims can satisfy the canons of rational analysis, those who press such claims can expect only the attention accorded to other superstitions. The question posed by the Paradox in Christ is, "Whose reason is to reign?" Is it the reasonableness of natural man who knows how the world goes, who knows that God helps those who help themselves, that there is no mercy for those who fall, and that strength is the sign of virtue? Or is it the reason of him whose life has been informed and redeemed by the touch of God in Christ? From the outside, our natural reason has already diagnosed the impossibility of this choice, and has closed the door to contradiction—and to life. Or so those say who have faced the paradox that we must be born anew, and who thereby have discovered the light by which they see light in what before was darkness.

When we speak of paradox within the context of the biblical faith, we can only ask: paradox for whom? The Christian makes no claim to speak acceptably to the standards of those who have not found the truth in

Christ. The ambiguity of the Christian's situation is that he finds both these persons inside himself. Simultaneously, he is the unredeemed and natural man who imposes his standards of truth and meaning to exclude paradox, and he is among the redeemed who have caught a glimpse of the new life; he sees the vision of the new life but finds it too difficult to sustain in all his ways of thinking and acting.

The presence of paradox in our thinking warns us that we must remember who we are, lest we be too easily swayed, and destroy ourselves either by embracing a false simplicity, or by missing the truth because it does not make the sense we expect to find. Of course this is ambiguous. All knowledge of fundamental things is ambiguous. The Christian faith does not promise to remove the ambiguities that haunt our lives as persons. It only promises a life that is grounded in the truth.

MYTH

IT is possible to frame a language in which no statement is ever ambiguous or mythical in its flavor. Mathematics does so. But in such a language there is no room for flights of fancy, no joyousness of exchange, no agony of decision, no glee in finding, no glory in being met, no haunting loss of that which, dimly seen, still eludes the grasp of words. Such a clearly fashioned language can have the austere elegance of logical form, but it contains no shades of meaning or hints of beauty yet unshared. There may be bitter struggle of the mind to fashion its speech into the pattern of a neutral proof, but no struggle of the living person cries through its words, for this is the stuff from which the speech of faith is fashioned. In the language of biblical faith, the full man speaks, not solely his rationality, and he speaks as one who knows and is known, who worships, and by his words shares with others his search for truth.

Tutored by our predilection for the scientific kind of statement, we expect to find also in the language of biblical faith the same neutral formulas that codify results. We anticipate that each sentence from the Bible or biblical theologians shall have a single meaning that clearly adds another brick to the solid structure of our knowledge. We want statements we can stand apart from to judge their truth or falsity. Instead, we are told a story, we are given a myth to recite, and in the reciting we find our imagination fired, our response captured, and our existence lifted up. At the end, when we are asked to state the truth we celebrated in the myth, we discover that our formulas cannot carry the freight of meaning we intend unless they too are flavored with the myth. So the creeds, for example, cannot stand as finished demonstrations, independently of the story whose point they symbolize.

The nature of myth appears in its function, not in its form as a literary style, or in its content as an account of origins or the doings of the gods and ancient heroes. And myth is not to be equated with an unscientific world view from which the Gospel must be freed. These definitions give the game back to popular speech where "mythical" is synonymous with "false."

A myth is a story used as an image. In the actions of the story, we recognize the relationships in which we live and the choices we have made. The story functions as an image because it points beyond itself to that larger world of relationships that sustains us. Simultaneously it presents that meaning to us and becomes the means by which we celebrate our participation in it.

As we recite the myth, its action invites us to discover new facets of experience; it arouses us to fresh possibilities of response and deeper problems of relationship, in a way that no flatly neutral description can do. By reciting the story, we become participants in it. The acts of its characters are our own; their purposes express our designs; with them we attain the full stature of man in the sight of God, or with them we hide from God's sight and voice. This is more than empathy because the myth, by imaging the reality, brings us into its presence so that through the actors of the story we also live and act. Their deeds become our deeds and their choices become ours. Their sin is our own sin, and their redemption is the promise of our own.

Such personal appropriations as those the myth opens to us could be reduced to flat propositions which embalm pieces of neutral cognitive knowledge, like insects preserved in amber. We could even link specific facts about our world of experience with details in the story. Perhaps we could name the characters and give the time and place where they were supposed to have lived and died. But while such literal facts would anchor the story in the common history of man, they do not constitute the power of the myth. Locating the power of the myth in its historicity guts the myth like a split fish, and its truth lies dead in our hands. The meaning then is gone, for meaning lies in action.

Myths confront us with actions to which we must respond by acting. Their truth is not static and neutral, but dynamic and passionately committed, and it grows out of confrontation, disclosure, and the dialogue of persons. The words that describe the myth take on its flavor as we speak. When we state its truth in clear and formal terms, we lose its meaning, because formal doctrines fail to communicate our adventure in discovery, and they excite no glow of response from those who hear.

It may be possible in scientific speech to exclude any tinge or flavor of myth. But the oftener and the more willingly we use the term "model" to describe our scientific understanding, the closer we come to framing myths for the service of science. The scientific model depicts the structure of the events we are exploring; it guides our action as we seek to know the nature of this portion of our world; it is an image, even when it is couched as a mathematical formula rather than as a narrative or as a physical picture.

Our use of models and myths reflects our ambiguity as persons. We know only in part; we see through a glass darkly; and our words and mathematical symbols are only shadows of what we see. While neither the meaning of the myth nor its truth can be precisely contained in a set of words, they can be appropriated by informed and imaginative rehearsal of the words. If, at the last, our language cannot give us the precision of final truth, it can release us from the burden of defending to the bitter and barren end the literal, unmythical truths of the words we have found.

THE TYRANNY OF WORDS

WITH all its dangers and obscurities, the mythical style in which biblical religion speaks saves us from two common errors in our use of religious language and in our attempt to identify the truth it carries. Both errors can be expressed in the same set of words: it is taking the language of biblical religion (including the creeds and formal theology) too literally, externally, impartially, and unambiguously, as if language in religion had the hard and glossy quality of truth that we mistakenly imagine it has in science. We commit both errors by mistaking the myth for that which it images.

One error is committed by those who find the style of the story too gross and earthy for scientifically informed men who know what the world is like. Snakes cannot talk; God does not live on a mountain top; he would not have chosen a particular people toward whom he was partial; our astronomy has no place where heaven could be; the fires of hell could do no harm to souls who have no bodies with which to feel pain; the processes of nature do not lead to the end of the world. If such terms represent the Christian and biblical faith, these objectors say, then honest men who live in a modern world must find other ways to declare their faith. This forthrightness must be respected, but they have thrown out the baby with the bath water.

The second error appears in the reluctance of some to drain the bath water because they have mislaid the baby. For these also, the terms of the myth have become literal truth in external, final terms, now to be defended in the precise words of the myth. Heaven is paved with gold, not platinum, and its gates are of pearl and not diamond; careful deciphering of the Scripture's code will reveal when and how all spirits, living and dead, will be raised up to meet the coming Lord in the air at the end of time. Unless the Lord descends from heaven like an astronaut returning to the earth—for he went *up* into heaven—his coming cannot be real at all. If any familiar phrase in the Bible is changed by a new translation, or any item challenged as a figure of speech, these people feel that the very truth itself is being denied. We mistake the point if we see this only as a crass and unenlightened textual literalism. Much more, it mistakes the words for the truth they image. And pious worship of an image, even though it be a verbal one, is idolatry.

The reply to both errors is the same. If we are to say anything, we must say something. The problem is to say it in a way that will lift up the truth we have caught, without binding us to the literal finality of the specific words we use. It is tempting to insist that we should restrict ourselves to exact and literal truth. But on what ground do we declare that a flat, prosaic account from which all action and participation of persons has been drained away is really the truth after all? Why is a scientific account presumed to be more literal than the myth? Why is the claim—made on purportedly scientific grounds—that man's fate is the silence of death and his only "immortality" is his contribution to the gene pool of the species through his offspring, truer than the claim that he will have a life with God in heaven? This "gene pool" can be no more precisely located than heaven itself. The real question is how we will relate ourselves to our own fate, and how we will meet the end that comes to all of us. We cannot say that heaven is a fiction because it is a myth, while biological immortality in the gene pool is true because it is a fact. Both of these—and other answers also—are equally myths insofar as they capture our imagination and enable us to participate as persons in the adventure which they image. What kind of destiny are we going to live by—one with hope and fulfillment both now and in the future with God, or one in which we only tread out a few witless years on the accelerating treadmill of time? We do not choose between fact and fiction, between truth and myth. We choose between myths, seeking that myth which images most lucidly and compellingly the truth that lures us. We can find our meaning in myths that image the unreality of personal acts and relationships, or in myths that make our personal selves authentic. At the end, we are brought not to the absence and denial of truth, but to face our responsibility for the quality of the truth we seek and accept.

As we seek a purer vision of what the myth images, and celebrate its meaning more fully, we are released from the tyranny of exact words. Myth does not release us from the necessity for accuracy; it does release us from the bondage to finality. The doctrine of the end of the world and the judgment which it brings is a myth. But the judgment is all the more real because we confront it in a story as well as in daily living. To those who object to the story—whether it takes the form of struggle and pain in a hostile world under the gloom that gathers as the light of Eden fades, or whether it stands in the glare of the end of time when evil is destroyed and a righteous world revels in the full rule of Christ—we can only say, "How would you say it? How would you speak of responsibility and judgment in terms that challenge and compel and invite our faith?" If you answer at all, you must tell a story, even though it be the story of a race long since a fossil in a world grown silent and cold in the changeless balance of complete entropy. And if you tell a story, you create another myth to image the destiny you believe to be our meaning as human persons.

Myth announces the truth which is created by persons acting in response to persons and a Person. The whole and fully literal truth lies beyond the power of our categories of analysis to capture or contain. Neither in the most formal statements of the creeds nor in our scientific laws have we succeeded in being literally or completely true. These too, are myths, brief recitals of the events by which we live. Scientific laws image an impersonal universe, unaware of our existence. The creeds image the acts of God on our behalf, and the truth that we can know only in our response to him. They do not tell us what he is. They do not define the "truths" we can know about him. By inviting us to respond, they image for us the truth we can know with him.

THE HIERARCHY OF KNOWLEDGE

WE end with the problem with which we began. Science gives us one way of understanding ourselves, and biblical religion gives us another. Each must maintain its integrity as a way of understanding our existence, for neither has any light to shed upon the problems we face unless it speaks strongly and uncompromisingly in its own terms.

We do live within a natural order whose patterns and processes constitute the matrix of our lives. However much we may wish to say that God created this order, it still has its own form and structure of relationships with which we must come to terms if we would work with the materials and realize the possibilities it provides us. We must learn what its processes are and what limits its patterns set. Without such knowledge we cannot accommodate our plans and intentions to the character of the natural order, and we must make the adjustment, for we do not actually control nature. We share this world with our fellows, therefore we reject the notion that knowledge of that world is something private and interior. On the contrary, knowledge of our common world must be the same for all who share in its processes and participate in its events, and this is the goal that science serves. Since the world seems to show no awareness of our being and expresses no concern for our personal fate, our scientific knowledge, even when it includes ourselves as part of the total picture of nature, necessarily is couched in the same impersonal, deterministic terms that state the order and regularity and law that we find in nature. But if this is all we have, we cease to be persons, and all other persons become with ourselves mere tools to meaningless ends.

We also live in a world of personal beings who reach out to meet us, who rejoice with us when we succeed and cherish us when we fail, who seek our good and sustain us by offering the resistance of their unique perceptions. In the insights of biblical religion this world is elevated and enlarged to include the being and action of God himself as that being before whom we cannot be less than persons who are fully responsible for the response they make. This world of personal beings, which contains as much of strife and competition as of love and supporting care, cannot be captured in the formulas of impartial knowledge we apply to the world of nature. We can know this world of personal relationships only as we share the life of exchange with all who constitute its body.

But these are not separate worlds. In the end, the world of personal beings and their relationships is also the world of nature. Therefore, we cannot take the easy road of saying that science deals with one part of our experience while biblical religion deals with another segment. Neither can we combine these knowledges into a single pattern embracing both, for each in its own way contradicts the other, and we cannot permit one to absorb the other so as to create a "religious" science or a "scientific" religion.

The warfare between science and biblical religion has become a warfare within ourselves as we strive to unite the purposes from which each grows. If we say of either body of knowledge that it has been simply given to us intact, we are denying the participation by which we know. We cannot say that nature imposes itself upon us and thereby gives us science; neither can we say that God thrusts himself upon us and thereby gives us the religion of the Bible. The shape our knowledge takes depends upon the ends we seek as we meet the mystery that surrounds us. In science, we try to reduce that mystery to law by standing aside to describe the world as it is without us, and we discover the most intractable mystery within ourselves as we try to find the laws in our own actions. In biblical religion, we find the mystery in God, whose approach to us withholds the security of knowledge structured in universal law, because he meets us as persons by being a Person whom we cannot ignore. On one side we have a security of knowledge but persons are gone from the picture. On the other side, we have the authenticity of personal being and action but no security of neutral knowledge by which to steer our course. In the one way of engaging the mystery of existence, we force ourselves and all other personal beings, including God, into the neutral forms of the world common to us all. In the other way of engaging the mystery that surrounds us, our personal and shifting appropriations of experience become the basis upon which we describe ourselves and the world and the actions of God.

Since our knowledge varies as we turn first in one direction and then in the other, it seems as if we are compelled to choose between knowledge and something else which cannot claim that title. One way of acting seems to produce knowledge and truth because they refer to that common structure which enfolds us all. In the other way of acting, knowledge and truth seem to be absent because we are proclaiming ourselves. If we make the choice for either form of action, alone, we deny the ambiguity within ourselves, and we turn the dialectic in knowledge into a warfare in which each way of understanding must secure a decisive victory over the other. If we permit that victory, we become selfless units or rootless selves, and either way we deny that we are persons surrounded by a world from which we take and to which we give in the economy of life.

The answer is not in the choice between knowledge and something else. The answer lies in enlarging our conception of knowledge to include all ways of responding by affirming the authenticity of our purposes, by accepting the responsibility for the ends we seek in knowing and for the specific pattern of response we employ to achieve those ends. As circumstances seem to indicate, and as our intentions require, we can act in different ways to enhance or to reduce the effect of our personal participation. In turn, our knowledge and understanding will vary in their form and in their content, but one style of knowing does not constitute authentic knowledge while the other represents its absence by being something other than knowledge. Both are cut from the same cloth despite the apparent differences in texture. As we move from the content of science and its methods of study to biblical religion and its personal appropriation, the degree of personal involvement in the resulting content shifts, but this does not signal a decrease in knowledge as it becomes more clearly personal. On the contrary, both science and biblical religion are equally authentic in their own terms, if we recognize the personal commitment and intention which underlies each one. Both represent human action toward different ends, and therefore both rest upon personal responsibility and participation in knowing.

When, in the light of this basis for our knowing, we array the fields of study from the most impersonal and abstract to the most personal and concrete, we no longer move from the truest and most dependable to the least true and least dependable. We are no longer imprisoned by the dogma that the more personal and concrete levels are sustained and guaranteed by the less personal and more universal levels below them.

The odd result is that a genuine hierarchy of knowledge does exist, with its support coming from above and not from below. In this hierarchy, each level of increasing impersonality and abstraction is supported and authenticated by the more personal and concrete declaration of the self above it. The structure of human knowledge, far from being a stable pyramid founded upon a solid grasp of an autonomous reality independent of man, is instead a web spun by faith. It is not even a pyramid standing on its apex, but a spider web of interconnecting strands of action and purpose which quivers with uncertainty when every new experience touches its threads. Where are the anchors from which faith has spun this web? Some have said that they are in nature as it exists independently of man, and others say in nothing, since there is no goal or pattern until we assert our own. Those within the biblical tradition say that faith anchors the web of knowledge in the acts and will of God. For as they have travelled its network and thrown out new strands to embrace their widening vision, they have found themselves within a community of persons, there met and supported by a Person who confirms and authenticates their own selfhood as persons.

✸

A SELECTED BIBLIOGRAPHY

UNLESS one is cursed with total recall, it is impossible for him to identify all the sources of his thought. The following are some of the books that I can identify as having been particularly useful to me in thinking through the issues between science and biblical religion. Therefore, this list by no means exhausts the body of relevant works, or pretends to be a representative sampling of the literature on the subject. I do not cite them here to prove my case, or to imply that other readers would necessarily come to my conclusions after reading any or all of them, but in the hope that other readers will also find them stimulating and fruitful—especially those with which the reader disagrees.

Ayer, Alfred J. *Language, Truth and Logic.* New York: Dover Publications, 1952.

Boulding, Kenneth. *The Image.* Ann Arbor: The University of Michigan Press, 1956.

Braithewaite, R. B. *An Empiricist's View of the Nature of Religious Belief.* Cambridge: The University Press, 1955.

Buber, Martin. *I and Thou.* Trans. Smith, Ronald Gregor. Edinburgh: T and T Clark, 1937.

Coulson, C. A. *Science and Christian Belief.* Chapel Hill: University of North Carolina Press, 1955.

Dodd, Charles H. *The Apostolic Preaching.* New York: Harper and Row, 1944.

Emmet, Dorothy M. *The Nature of Metaphysical Thinking.* London: Macmillan, 1953.

Ferré, Frederick. *Language, Logic and God.* New York: Harper and Row, 1961.

Flew, Antony, and Macintyre, Alasdair. (eds.) *New Essays in Philosophical Theology.* London: SCM Press, 1955.

Foster, Michael B. *Mystery and Philosophy.* London: SCM Press, 1957.

Frank, Philipp. *Philosophy of Science.* Englewood Cliffs, N.J.: *Prentice-Hall,* 1957.

Greene, John C. *The Death of Adam.* Ames: Iowa State University Press, 1959.

Hanson, N. R. *Patterns of Discovery.* New York: Cambridge University Press, 1958.

Heim, Karl. *Christian Faith and Natural Science.* New York: Harper and Row, 1953.

————. *The Transformation of the Scientific World View.* New York: Harper and Row, 1953.

————. *The World: Its Creation and Consummation.* Edinburgh: Oliver and Boyd, 1962.

Heisenberg, Werner. *Physics and Philosophy: The Revolution in Modern Science.* New York: Harper and Row, 1958.

Hick, John. *Faith and Knowledge.* Ithaca, N.Y.: Cornell University Press, 1957.

Hordern, William. *Speaking of God.* New York: Macmillan, 1964.

Hunter, Archibald M. *Introducing New Testament Theology.* London: SCM Press, 1957.

————. *The Message of the New Testament.* Philadelphia: Westminster, 1944.

Macmurray, John. *Persons in Relation.* London: Faber and Faber, 1961.

————. *The Self As Agent.* London: Faber and Faber, 1957.

Mascall, E. L. *Christian Theology and Natural Science.* New York: Ronald Press, 1956.

Moreau, Jules L. *Language and Religious Language.* Philadelphia: Westminster, 1961.

Niebuhr, H. Richard. *The Meaning of Revelation.* New York: Macmillan, 1941.

———. *Radical Monotheism and Western Culture.* New York: Harper and Row, 1943.

Niebuhr, Reinhold. *The Nature and Destiny of Man.* New York: Charles Scribner's Sons, 1941, 1943.

Niebuhr, Richard R. *Revelation and Historical Reason: A Study in Theological Method.* New York: Charles Scribner's Sons, 1957.

Ogden, Schubert, *Christ Without Myth.* London: Collins, 1962.

Polanyi, Michael. *Personal Knowledge: Towards a Post-Critical Philosophy.* Chicago: University of Chicago Press, 1958.

———. *Science, Faith and Society.* London: Oxford University Press, 1946; Chicago: University of Chicago Press (Phoenix, P155), 1964.

———. *The Study of Man: The Lindsay Memorial Lectures.* London: Routledge and Kegan Paul, 1959; Chicago: University of Chicago Press (Phoenix P128), 1959.

Pollard, William G. *Chance and Providence: God's Action in a World Governed by Scientific Law.* New York: Charles *Scribner's Sons,* 1958.

Ramsey, Ian T. *Religious Language.* London: SCM Press, 1957.

Reichenbach, Hans. *The Rise of Scientific Philosophy.* Berkeley: University of California Press, 1956.

Richardson, Alan. *An Introduction to the Theology of the New Testament.* London: SCM Press, 1958.

———. (ed.) *A Theological Word Book of the Bible.* New York: Macmillan, 1950.

Schilling, Harold K. *Science and Religion: An Interpretation of Two Communities.* New York: Charles Scribner's Sons, 1962.

Shideler, Mary McDermott. *The Theology of Romantic Love: A Study in the Writings of Charles Williams.* New York: Harper and Row, 1962.

Smethurst, Arthur F. *Modern Science and Christian Beliefs.* New York: Abingdon, 1957.

Storer, John H. *The Web of Life.* New York: New American Library, 1956.

Teilhard de Chardin, Pierre. *The Phenomenon of Man.* New York: Harper and Row, 1959.

Tillich, Paul. *The Courage To Be.* New Haven: Yale University Press, 1952.

———. *Systematic Theology.* Chicago: University of Chicago Press, 1951, 1957.

White, Andrew Dickson. *A History of the Warfare of Science With Theology in Christendom.* New York: D. Appleton and Co., 1903.

Whitehead, Alfred North. *Science and the Modern World.* New York: Macmillan, 1925.

Whorf, Benjamin Lee. *Language, Thought and Reality.* New York: John Wiley and Sons, 1956.

Zuurdeeg, Willem. *An Analytical Philosophy of Religion.* New York: Abingdon, 1958.

INDEX